NUMBER 11

New American Review

A Touchstone Book
Published by
Simon and Schuster

Distributed in UK and British Commonwealth
by Secker & Warburg

NEW AMERICAN REVIEW
Editor: Theodore Solotaroff
Poetry Editor: Richard Howard
Associate Editor: Lawrence Alson
Assistant to the Editor: Irene Pavincich

Production Associates: Lee Hochman, Sharon Hurley,
   Veronica Johnson, Irene Kask, Terence McCabe

Cover design by Fred Otnes

FIRST PRINTING

SBN 671-20837-3
Library of Congress Catalog Card Number: 67-27377
Manufactured in the United States of America

The editors invite submissions. Manuscripts will
not be returned unless accompanied
by stamped self-addressed envelope.

Contents

EDITOR'S NOTE 7

Allen Ginsberg, From *These States* 9
M. F. Beal, *Gold* 13
Cynthia Macdonald, *Instruction from Bly* 29
Walter Abish, *Hesse, Part One; Hesse, Part Two* 31
Michael Rossman, *The Day We Named Our Child*
We Had Fish for Dinner 33
Frank Stanford, *The Gospel Bird* 48
Frances Starr, *Dont Talk to Me About War* 50
Allen Wiggins, *Earnest Remarks, Not Literature* 54
John Clayton, *Richard Brautigan: The Politics of*
Woodstock 56
William Matthews, *Five Poems*
      BALL AND CHAIN, YES INDEED 69
      HARD STUFF 69
      NIGHT DRIVING 70
      SUPPOSE 70
      SLEEP 71
James Kempton, *Dare to Struggle, Dare to Win* 73
Stanley Plumly, *Karate* 79
Paul Spike, *A Good Revolution* 80
Rudy Kikel, *Going* 93
Norman Martien, *Getting Out of Schools* 96
A. J. Litwinko, *Letter to His Brother* 117
John Morgan, *The Dark Ajar* 118
Paul West, *The Season of the Single Women* 119
Robert Chatain, *Veins* 130
W. S. Merwin, *The Wharf* 131
Robert Coover, *The Last Quixote* 132

Steve Katz, *A Home-Cooked Meal for The Astronaut* 144
Daryl Hine, *Ego Loss* 161
James Merrill, *The Victor Dog* 162
Harold Ober, *Daddy* 164
Hilma Wolitzer, *Ending* 175
Marilyn Hacker, *For Elektra* 182
Irving Feldman, *As Fast As You Can* 184
Larry Rubin, *The Messenger* 186
Nicholas von Hoffman, *Nixon* 187

THE WRITER'S SITUATION: III 202
    Introduction 202
    Benjamin DeMott 203
    Stanley Kauffmann 205
    Alvin Greenberg 211
    Hilton Kramer 217
    Richard Hugo 221
    Neil Compton 225

Sylvia Plath, *Last Words* 232

CORRESPONDENCE 233

CONTRIBUTORS 236

Editor's Note

BEGINNING WITH *this issue*, NAR *will be published by Simon and Schuster. Its founding publisher, New American Library, has kept it going for ten issues. That's a strong show of support for a paperback magazine: in the past twenty years, only* New World Writing, *also sponsored by New American Library, was sustained for any longer than that, and the others have been discontinued after only a few issues. So, the editors of NAR are grateful for this backing as well as for that offered now by Simon and Schuster.*

There are no doubt different reasons why paperback magazines—several of them quite excellent ones—have been so short-lived. But I think their main problem grows out of their particular purpose and value—that of bringing an abundance of significant writers, often relatively unknown ones, to the attention of a wide audience. This, in turn, means large printings, broad distribution, a low cover price, and, as a consequence, a strong and continuing sale. In short, what is essentially a thick "little magazine" has to make its way in the very crowded and very fickle world of mass-market paperbacks, where "volume" is king and "impulse" its agent. When a new paperback magazine appears, there may be enough curiosity about it to sustain an adequate volume, but once it becomes more or less familiar, this impulse begins to flag, and the magazine sooner or later begins its reverse journey, in the form of "returns," from the mass market to the publisher and into oblivion.

This is a simplified explanation, but the thrust of it is all too clear and pointed. To keep NAR going we shall have to retrench a bit. One way will be to reduce our printings and distribute them more selectively. This means that NAR will be more available in bookstores and less in drugstores, five-and-tens, etc. Another way will be to go back to our initial three-times-a-year schedule. Finally, we shall have to acquire more of that kind of reader support that paperbacks do not have but magazines cannot do without: subscriptions. So, if you feel that NAR has earned your support, we truly need it.

Otherwise, NAR will continue to be what it has been: a journal that tries to stay open to the flow of fresh, articulate writing and thought. As I have said before, our issues are planned as little as possible, the idea being to place the initiative where it most appropriately and productively belongs—out there, in the culture and with the writers, rather than in here, with the editor, his "stable," his New York seismograph. As it happened, much of the flow of interesting work that has come our way the past spring, when this issue was being prepared, originated in that "other place," to use John Clayton's phrase for Richard Brautigan's locale, known also by such names as "the Movement," "the counter-culture," "the new underground." So, we've put all of that writing together in this issue, allowing the essays, stories, and some of the poems to touch, comment, and resonate off each other. The result is a substantial, if hardly comprehensive, account of that extraordinary strain of new experience, imagination, and risk—each nurturing the others—that is coming to the surface today in America and defining itself.

TS

From
These States

Allen Ginsberg

A VOW

I will haunt these States
    with beard bald head
    eyes staring out plane window,
    hair hanging in Greyhound bus midnight
leaning over taxicab seat to admonish
        an angry cursing driver
        hand lifted to calm
          his outraged vehicle
that I pass with the Green Light of common law.

Common Sense, Common law, common tenderness
        & common tranquillity
our means in America to control the money munching
        war machine, bright lit industry
everywhere destroying forests & excreting soft pyramids
    of newsprint, Redwood and Ponderosa patriarchs
    silent in Meditation murdered & regurgitated as smoke,
      sawdust, screaming ceilings of Soap Opera,
    thick dead Lifes, slick Advertisements
        for Gubernatorial big guns
      burping Napalm on palm rice tropic greenery.

9

Dynamite in forests,
> boughs fly slow motion,
>> thunder down ravine,
>> Helicopters roar over National Park, Mekong Swamp,
>> Dynamite fire blasts thru Model Villages,
Violence screams at Police, Mayors get mad over radio,
> Drop the Bomb on Niggers!
>> drop Fire on the gook China
>>> Frankenstein Dragon
>> waving its tail over Bayonne's domed Aluminum
>>>>>>> oil reservoir!

I'll haunt these States all year
> gazing bleakly out train windows, blue airfield
>> red TV network on evening plains,
> decoding radar Provincial editorial paper message,
> deciphering Iron Pipe laborers' curses as
>> clanging hammers they raise steamshovel claws
>> over Puerto Rican agony lawyers' screams in slums.

October 11, 1966

SONORA DESERT-EDGE

>   Om A Hum Vajra Guru
>   Padma Siddhi Hung
>   —Drum from Gary
>   from Tarthang Tulku

Brown stonepeaks   rockstumps
                    cloudless sunlight
Saguaro green arms praying up
          spine ribs risen
                         woodpecker-holed
          nose-pricked limbs
              lifted salutation—
orange flower eyes lifted on
          needley Ocotillo stalk
Jumping Cholla pistils closing pollined
     eyebrow-vagina buds to the
          poked pinkey—
Palo Verde smooth forked branch
          above prickly-pear ears

Smoke plumed up white
     from scratched desert plain,
     chemical smoke, military copper
     airplanes rotting,
          4% Copper Smelter smog

—in wire cage, ivory hook-beaked
                    round pupil eyed
     Bald Eagle's head, tailfeathers
     hung below claw'd branch, symmetric
body plumes brown webbed like dollarbills,
     insecticides sterilized many
               adults

—green duck neck sheen spectral as
          moon machines
Raven hopping curious black beaked

Coyote's nose sensitive lifted to air
          blinking eye sharp
as the rose bellied Cardinal's ivory whistle

—tiny bright statues of Buddha
          standing,
     blue desert valley haze—
     cactus lessons in sentience,
Trees like mental carrots—Anaconda
     smelters   white plumesmoke in
     San Manuel, or Phelps-Dodge
     in Douglas?—
Yellow'd Creosote bushes in granular
     dust, hills jeep tracked,
Prairie dogs stand quivering-spined in
     cactus-shade.   A museum,
     minds in Ashramic City—tweetling
     bird radios—Hopi Rain:

April 29, 1969

Gold

M. F. Beal

Where, When, What:

I've been here almost two months now. I've been staying most of the time, all but the warmest nights, with friends: Evelyn and Peter. Friends, but not old friends; they're far away, some dead, even. Some might not realize I count them that. I'm hoping to see Ruth. I came here in the first place looking for Ruth. It doesn't make me proud to say that; but it's true. I had been looking for her up and down the coast when I heard she was here, too, on the opposite hillside. So I stayed.

Settling down like this has set me to thinking for the first time about why I—we—all left the city. It's almost as if a whole generation has seen itself unable to cope, or as if there has been some sort of pestilence to which certain people are hideously sensitive. That's how it must seem, at any rate, to those deserted. For me it was a simple decision: one night returning from work I realized if I opened the door to my apartment I would be there till I died; so I spent the night with a friend, thinking of how I had, now, to abandon the city and look for Ruth. Or perhaps the search for Ruth was a motive I attached to my decision to justify it.

Her name comes up, of course, fairly often, although generally people on this side of the valley do not visit with and are not overly concerned with the people on the other side of the valley. A curious business. Is it jealousy? It really doesn't seem so. Call it preoccupation with the everyday; life itself is the big preoccupation here—except, of course, for gold. Gold. Continual talk of gold.

But though I am so little interested in that part of this life, everyone is very polite. No one pays too much attention to me; or rather, just enough. The attention, when it

13

comes, is practical, relating to the business of the valley (life): Evelyn dispenses it mainly, and indirectly, like this: "Did you notice?" she asks, or "Have you ever tried? . . ." Of course it's perfectly reasonable to presume I'm here for salvation—all the rest are.

Ruth and the Mountain:

I've been trying, today, to remember the hike I took up the mountain the first week here. I have a bad memory. I believe I wanted to orient myself; but I may have been feeling bored, and trapped—isn't that really more likely? It was still May. The nights were cold. I had quite a lot of equipment I'd brought with me in a leather satchel I got in a secondhand store down the street from where I lived the day I decided to start looking for Ruth; a Gladstone bag, the proprietor called it. The evening before my hike up the mountain I went from shack to cabin to shelter and begged a packboard, a hand axe, a canteen; Evelyn gave me rice, my sneakers would do, Peter lent me a sweater to wear under my shirt, so I wouldn't have to lug my jacket along. I also had a bail-handled pot, remnant from a boy scout kit; ditto spoon, extra socks, tea, matches, a geologist's pick, several small bags for collecting specimens of rock and plants, a magnifying glass, a handbook of minerals and one of birds, cigarettes, a blanket roll. What else?

It was a fine day but I got a late start. The mountain was very impressive, bleak with sunlight. Our two hillsides fingering down from her and the rope of water most think is responsible for the gold stood clearly on her flank like children against their mother. But this mother was no insipid aproned lady; rather a sturdy black woman, basalt heaped from her brow, scoria trailing dark hair streaks in a perfect forty-five-degree cape. Only where our creek cut was orange limonite exposed like a tear. A track led to her top.

A Snapshot:

I could not help but think that in other days there would have been a snapshot of me, standing by the last trees, sunlight splashed on the gray dust. It would have shown me in Levis, slender, looking not at the camera but into the branches above. The only thing I cannot see as I develop this snapshot in my mind is the expression my face would wear.

Now the Mountain Herself:

Suddenly the mountain loomed enormous. Where water cut rock the newly exposed basalt was like gashes in her flesh. Viewed afar, from the hillside, she was after one week already familiar; but now as I loomed on her she loomed back. There was a quality in the air like lemon—thin, sharp. It had been only minutes since I decided not to pack the canteen's two pounds of water; but now it had receded in my awareness as if I were some Eocene horse with his three toes who had decided not to wear a man's saddle on his back. I was dislodged, unbraced, overmounted.

A Lava Flow to Negotiate:

I knew man had been here before me by the brightness of the track. But the black lava flow, dodging from the mountain's broken top, left behind a blanket twenty, thirty feet thick, a blanket to bury the sandals of an Indian out away from his camp hunting elk. I sat to smoke and imagine what I would have done in his place.

Some Sort of Rabbit:

As I sat virtually immobile, my cigarette just inches from my face and setting free fine veils of smoke, I saw dots of movement, points, shifts of light in the ropy black rock. At first I thought it was some peculiarity of the rough-surfaced lava flow; but then I realized it was a number of small animals, many of them shifting and moving in their burrows and runs as my presence faded from their memories. Or had they been moving right along, simply counting on me not to notice them in my preoccupation with being myself? The lava face was shimmering with them, finally, going about their business of living in the crisp, decaying rock. There was an occasional tiny piping, and once a landslide of such delicate proportions it could not have consisted of more than three or four grains of cinder. The longer I watched, the more clearly I could see these little animals: their large bright eyes; a habit of squatting briefly on hind legs every few steps; even visits from one to another and small courtesies of the path—nose-touching, touching of feet, squeaking. Suddenly it became embarrassing, almost frightening to eavesdrop and I stood, sending them instantly to ground.

A Banging:

I was now aware of all sorts of life signs as I continued. The path wound at the lava flowside for a bit, the dust pocked with footprints of birds, of the tiny animals; then it climbed steeply in a series of rough steps, finally coming out on a plateau. From this height I hoped to have my first sensation of having covered ground.

The trees, unfortunately, hid the valley below with its hillsides, and the stream which cut the valley was hidden too. It seemed I would have to cut back around the flank of the mountain to be above the valley again. So I was pleased when the track turned not much farther on and headed to a fair-sized clump of wizened alpine fir.

Then, as I reached the firs, I heard a banging. The wind was fresher the higher I climbed, and sound traveled more distinctly in the clear air, so as I walked the rustle and clatter of tree limbs far below drafted to me. But the banging was definitely extraordinary.

Not much farther I discovered the cabin. It was more of a shed, really, the tiniest house I had ever seen, and weathered deep-gray like rock. It stood in a level spot almost in the center of the trail; on all sides the ground sloped, which made it seem that someone's hand had flattened the spot. The door was open, banging; it was such a startling sound I had to go shut it immediately.

Inside was a bed, almost full-size, *made up with sheets and blankets.* Yet, where the sheets had been turned down were brown sausages of pack-rat droppings. There was a rocker, badly weathered, the back repaired with strips of rawhide, one rocker resting in a clutter of old clothing which seemed to have been dropped in flight, then rained on, then dried again and again to a stiff bas-relief. On a small oil-drum stove was a coffeepot. A table held a single cup with tacky rime of coffee residue, and (by far the neatest, most considered item of all) a white handkerchief heaped with nuggets of a metallic mineral. Now I say "a metallic mineral," but actually it was clear to me it was a pile of gold nuggets. And yet it couldn't be a pile of gold, for that defied logic; who would leave gold like that? so it became immediately in my mind "a metallic mineral," probably iron pyrites: "fool's gold."

I sat in the chair, before the empty, dirty cup and the neat pile of nuggets, as if that would make of me somehow the anchorite who had lived in this shack, and tried to imagine why he had left, abandoned his retreat. What had he seen, what thought had driven him from his haven?

A heavy depression came over me. I shut the door firmly, and put my face to the trail.

I Think I Took Water from the Spring Nearby:

Or I may have gotten it as I crossed the stream somewhat farther on. I was preoccupied the whole time thinking of the apartment that first Ruth and then I had abandoned, leaving, I remember, some of my clothes, letters (not Ruth's—those I gave her late one night), books, records; everything whose ideas had been outgrown and, just as important, for which there wasn't room in the back of the car. These thoughts had the effect of deadening me to the passage of time and the weight of the pack and it was not too long before I came to the rock fault.

A Big Smile:

I came suddenly on the crack, first narrow but opening over the next hundred feet surprisingly fast, as if the mountain were a vast chocolate pudding which had dried and split. The gash, with its delicate edges—tiny replicas of the larger split—was deep as well, perhaps twenty feet as it opened out. It lay along the mountainside like a big smile, bisected by the stream which must have teased it forth, and from which came the water the people below thought was the catalyst for the formation of gold . . .

Still, I'm remembering this—I'm sure at the time I didn't think it all. I wanted to get to the top. It had become a passion, and I had an hour's walking to go. I dropped my pack, setting it beside the mountain's smile.

Immediately I felt a foot taller and as if my stride were a yard long. Even the ache in my calves diminished. The tuff slid as I dug my toes into it, but still I made good progress; and before I thought it possible, I was within a few feet of the basalt nipple of the mountain peak. Then, like a gift, I found the track again, winding with footholds to the very summit. There, with the heavy blasting wind of early evening on my back, I stood in the fading sun and surveyed what I had done.

Where:

For the first time I could see the valley and the hillsides. The distortion of distance and the shadow which had overtaken them already leached all color from the tiny cabins; there were a few dots I thought might be people, but unlike the conies on the lava flow, concentration didn't bring them into clearer focus. Again I felt the depression of eavesdropping, of seeing aimless patterns in what must be to the people purposeful actions. I forced myself to watch, however, until the notion of patterns separated from the rest of my perceptions as tangerine skin does from the pulp, and the dots that were people came to represent something akin to points of electricity, energy. This perception gave me pleasure, a feeling of inward smiling. I could feel it travel through my organs as a tightening and warming, until my extremities tingled pleasantly. I was not able to refine my perceptions further.

So I turned on my heels and enjoyed the sensation of being clearly higher than anyone or anything for miles and miles. To the east, I saw flat plains and yellow desert; to the west, snow-tendriled peaks, lower than mine, shadowed. The sun, setting into the sheeted ocean, was pure gold.

Below, the gash in the mountainside was a definite smile—deep, black-toothed. The creek which split it moved with white leapings and a foamy urgency from an unprepossessing lens of snow that I realized must be deeper than it seemed. Then farther down, the beard of trees, with a cheek-patch to the side that entirely hid the cabin; and far, far below, the valley, the hillsides where the people, where Ruth was. Overall, a monumental sighing of the wind, blasting at the mountain's bald summit-nipple. I shivered. I started down.

When:

That was in May. I have described it at length, because now it seems to have been responsible for all that has followed—it must be what is responsible. But it is a mystery and you must interpret; I know no more about it than I've just told. When I point to the smiling gash of the fault and ask a friend what he thinks of *that*, he smiles and turns away, as if I am still, unfortunately, too preoccupied with appearances.

This Is Really a Diary:

But even a diary is selective: in the interval between the event and the transcription of it the mind closes itself to much. I could write as if I had rushed from each event to these pages, and then you might *feel* the immediacy; but it would be no more honest than to allow you a sensation of interval. So that is what I have done. Now here is something that happened today: one of the women who has been on the other hillside quite awhile without success, but who has followed the diet, meditated, etc., thought she passed some gold. By the time the story got to our hillside, she was said to have passed a nugget. Evelyn and Peter came up to tell me. I was working on my shelter, having gotten together, somehow, enough tools all at one time to nail up a few boards. But they were so excited (neither has passed any crystals yet) it was really unthinkable to continue pounding, so we talked the afternoon out. Very little gold has been passed on our hillside—why, no one knows. A few theories:

The average age of the people over here is higher; we are more uptight and can't release body-energy in pure form; some of us take too mechanical an attitude toward the formation of gold.

The chemical balance of the herbs, etc., which are considered vital to production of gold, is not the same as on the other hillside.

The chemical balance of the water is different.
We get more sunlight than they do.
Etc., etc.

I was also told to use the correct terminology: the crystals are called *calculi;* they are small regular crystals of gold, sometimes occurring with traces of chemically bonded minerals. I can understand the importance of correct terminology: because of the nature of what is occurring here, it is necessary to have a rational approach to the dissemination of information about it, especially with outsiders.

Late in the afternoon a messenger came over to say it had been a false alarm. The woman had not passed a gold calculus, but rather a common ammonium one.

Thinking of the woman on the other hillside made me wonder about Ruth. Among the things I ask myself often: is she living with someone? (Sometimes this is so painful a thought I can only hold it in my head for a moment at a time. Sometimes it doesn't bother me at all.) Does she think of me? Is she happy? (Also sometimes a painful thought.) As the messenger spoke of the woman's failure to produce a gold calculus I wanted to ask him whether the woman's name was Ruth. But I couldn't. Yet I immediately decided it was Ruth, and I thought of her trying, failing to pass a gold calculus. I was sorry for her pain, but I was happy she had failed; I must admit that. I was happy. That quality about Ruth, her solidness around some center of self-understanding, or if you will, self-acceptance, was always so painful to me, such a reproach. When I was most miserably unsure, she closed around her center like a clam. It served her right that she had failed, for once.

Gold!

Now here is what happened, what it is like to pass a calculus of gold. On the night described above, tired, sick with loneliness, I decided to fast for a week. Evelyn gathered a bitter weed she calls *pooha* and I ate it; it cleaned my system. The following day I did little but sit in the sun, defecate, try not to think about food. I could feel my body drying, the tissues squeezing from them the excess fluids and poisons of my life. I drank, all day, two cupfuls of water from the creek.

The next day I still thought of food, but it was a vague concern. I felt weak, and when I came out of the sun, chill. My body shook with chill all night; but, strangely, I slept deeply between the waking moments, and had no bad dreams.

Toward evening of the third day, I felt my hunger drop from me like a weight and my head became so clear it was painful. I was able to concentrate fully on parts of my life that have shamed me most: on my time with Ruth, and the things she and I did to each other, on my fear of my mother and father, my fear of becoming a father. I found also that if I turned toward the mountain and looked up-hill, I got again the inward smiling sensation I had had that day on her top. As if she was trying—ridiculous as it looks on paper—to tell me something. Some linkage, some congruence of mountain/humans whose meaning would fall open like a Chinese puzzle at the right touch—but I could only look and enjoy the tingling warmth on my limbs, focusing my thoughts occasionally on the colony of conies I had seen and thinking how I related to them as the mountain to us. This clarity lasted almost an hour. Afterward, I fell asleep in the sun and slept for a long time, waking only after sunset with a racking chill. Fortunately Evelyn and Peter came up to check on me, and immediately dressed me in all my clothing. Peter brought up some extra blankets and sat with me until I slept. I remember fragments of what he said: He was depressed about his inability to pass a calculus, even a common one. I tried to reassure him, to tell him how much I admired his relationship with Evelyn, and how solid he seemed to me. This time, in my fever and the clarity given me by the fasting, I was able to admire without also hating; and I told him as final reassurance something which leapt to my head, and which I suddenly realized my father used to say to me: *To him who hath, it shall be given . . . and from him who hath not, it shall be taken away.*

The fourth day I slept.

The fifth day I felt great energy and walked to the stream, where I washed myself with the fine black sand that bedded the shallows and rinsed myself over and over with the icy water. Then I sat shielded by a shadberry bush and let the sun dry me. I found myself remembering the neatly heaped pile of gold (it seemed clearly that, now) I had seen in the cabin on the mountain. Why had I not taken it? Because it belonged to *him*. But then why had he abandoned it?

The morning of the sixth day I woke in pain, cramps in my abdomen so severe I could not stretch out. Evelyn rubbed my back, which helped for a while; but then the pain became so deep and cutting that I couldn't stand to be touched. I tried not to cry out; but the pervasive cramps made me moan and I begged a hand to hold. There were many hands; there were many visitors. Evelyn bathed my face with cloths wrung out of water from the stream. At night a fire was built and the waiting continued. Finally the pain assumed a pulse; bad moments but then better ones during which I caught my breath. During the bad times I cried out freely, and the better times were such a relief that tears came to my eyes. At the end, Peter helped me to stand and we moved to the outer circle of firelight. There the calculus tore my body and passed out.

I slept.

When I woke I had a porridge, a thick gruel of some kind, and slept again.

To be without pain, to be able to sleep, is like divinity.

The Responsibility of Producing a Calculus:

Some of the people who have been here a long time produce calculi once a week, or a series of calculi over a period of hours every month or so. This is why, of course, it is possible for all of us to devote ourselves to the production of calculi; the gold is exchanged for what we need, and while there isn't an abundance there is enough for everyone to be comfortable. Peter also told me I can get money to visit the city, if I want to. He pointed out with considerable pride that while the colony has been in existence for almost fifteen (!) years, no one has had to work out for wages for almost ten. This is not true of other colonies which you may have heard about.

On the other hand, even a regular producer of calculi

can undergo a change which stops the process. Everyone seems to believe the deposition begins with a "seed," perhaps a particle of silt. Some claim more calculi are produced in the rainy season, when the stream is slightly cloudy. Some even eat small quantities of silt from the limonite clay bank exposed by the stream. No one knows anything definite about the rest of the process. It may be the water which acts as a catalyst, or something in the *pooha* herb we all eat; it may be the rice, the fasting, the meditation. There are a few who refuse to discuss the process at all, saying it is mystical and not to be plumbed at risk of unbalancing the active forces.

One final point of agreement is that the crystallization process takes a while to get going; all the calculi so far have been regular crystals ranging in size from barely visible to an inch across. This tends to place a value on patience, and in fact the regular producers have all been here many months, if not years. If you lack patience, you move on, for it is an ascetic life; perhaps this, too, has something to do with producing.

So It's Clear I Am an Initiate:

Today people visited me as if I were some kind of display. Many of them—other initiates—take my hand and grasp it lingeringly to tell me something they cannot put into words, looking me in the eyes, almost kissing me. Once or twice this has given me a chill, as if they know something about this business of producing calculi I don't yet know; they are so deeply into this gold thing—more, much more, than I am. It is almost as if they realize we are all only vessels. One of the men (young, though with broad streaks of gray at his temples and fingered into his beard) drew me schemata of the arrangement of atoms within a calculus. It is a crystalline conglomerate, not a pure crystal (in which the pattern of atoms is repeated without variation), nor amorphous (with no regularity of pattern), but something between: small clusters of crystals oriented in different ways. I was taken by his fluency in describing the phenomenon. This was certainly virtually all there was to know in terms of description. But what of all that lay beyond the naming? What of the why or how? When I framed my observations I got a quick, sharp, almost cautionary look back. So I turned to watching his mouth as he talked, the upper teeth hitting his lower lip and at the junction, beads of opaque spittle, almost a foam, springing up, stretching with the next mouth movement, breaking as if he were a fevered dog, a froth of fever working its way into the corner of the mouth before it was licked away.

But most who come to see me wear a face of fatigued gentleness.

Ruth: At Last.

I was sitting on the stoop in front of my half-completed shelter and my eyes were drawn by the form of a woman, heavy-bellied, slow, moving herself and her unborn child up the hill to visit me. Her legs beneath the hem of her dress were slender and she held her arms around her stomach as if trying to carry her load in a more wonted fashion. Her brown hair swept from side to side like the pendulum of a clock. I recognized her immediately: Ruth.

In the instant of recognition I was horrified to think my desire for her might flood back, but lowering myself into consideration of my state of mind, I found instead a clean emptiness. (By the time I knew this she had greeted me.) We sat side by side on the stoop like acquaintances on a park bench; I couldn't see her eyes.

"I'm living on the other hillside with John," she announced. She leaned back against the shelter frame when I said nothing and with the set of her shoulders added: *this thing I am doing now is not conditional.*

Conditional. I understood a great deal suddenly about her and me: and how our being together was never anything but conditional. Then she turned her face to me and her eyes said: *I am no longer an object.*

I said with my arms opening and resting on my thighs: *do you remember the warmth of my body, my presentness?*

"You can see a lot here we can't see on the other hillside," she said. "You can see up the mountain where the stream begins; the hill hides that from us."

"There is a fault up there, where the stream comes out of the ice-pack."

"A fault?" But she had already said what she came to say

and did not want to learn anything; she turned her head aside.

"What sort of person is John?"

She hesitated a long time—about a month, I guess, or at least a season of the mind, something like passing from spring into summer. "I have passed calculi. I am pregnant. I am happy."

I had to laugh. "You don't sound very happy."

"Well, I am. It's hard to explain, but I think more deeply about these things now. I don't just answer the first thing that enters my head."

This made me very sad. I sat looking up to the gashed smile at the mountaintop, at the black and wrinkled lips of the old lady with her basalt brow.

We talked for a long time, but that is all we said; and when the sun tilted over the old lady's head, Ruth went back to her man.

Pilgrim's Progress:

I awoke desperate to read. There wasn't so much as a book at Peter and Evelyn's, but they said there might be some down in the valley. I went from cabin to cabin: nothing. Finally, hard by the stream I saw a young man— really a child—whose face I knew, and introduced myself; and he took me to his shelter (which in its simplicity and starkness reminded me so much of my own, yet seemed so poor it almost made me cry) and on a shelf, next to his shaving mirror and razor, was *Pilgrim's Progress.*

"I got that because it has such far-out pictures in it, and here, look at this—" He took down a small reproduction of a painting by Gauguin that stood tilted against the wall behind his razor: *Jacob Wrestles with the Angel or Vision After the Sermon.* We stood and looked at it. The left side of the canvas held a curve of Breton peasant women, their white headcloths and dark dresses like the uniforms of a religious order, their superstitious faces open in wonder, while on the right Jacob wrestled with the Angel. The Angel's wings were strong, sweeping over Jacob, whose arms, inferior wings, knotted in the effort of fending off God's Angel. There wasn't even a suggestion that Jacob would win.

I took *Pilgrim's Progress* and headed back to my shelter thinking about the boy who had somewhere found this book and the Gauguin print. Just old enough to have been born in the valley, he was one of the few children there. Like them, he couldn't read. I had never been bothered by this: what need, really, was there for reading? But now it distressed me. How would it be possible to understand what happened, knowing less than man did already? As I read, Peter and Evelyn's three dogs came sniffing uphill to see what I was doing and sat down with me. I saw them as distinctly, then, as I would humans: Sam (for Samuel Gompers), Emmett (for Emmett Till), and the puppy, Ché. Sam, oldest of the three, thrust his nose in my hand and moved along under its weight, humping his back and groaning to me to scratch the thick fur of his rump, beating his tail against my leg when I stopped, squinting his eyes shut and panting when I scratched. Ché tumbled whining, clicking his milk teeth together, stump tail furiously beating the stones; Sam snapped, Ché fell back abashed; Emmett set to licking himself noisily, tonguing the bald globes of his testicles, sniffing, inspecting, scratching, yawning. In the city, I had had a dog who smelled sour, strong; these dogs, with their diet of brown rice and *pooha*, smell like a child's stuffed toy. As I saw them in this manner, so vividly, it seemed for a long moment that they were wise in some inscrutable way, that they were teachers. And that was delightful, but frightening, too, because it seemed to tell me about myself. Was I mad? Or had I stumbled on some perfectly reasonable awareness? The word *conditional* leapt to the front of my thoughts; these animals seemed anything but conditional, so firmly were they tied to everything around them. They were dependent and yet independent, accepting the warmth of the sun and my hand as if sun and hand were equal in some equation.

But a Man Is Not a Dog:

I am unable to avoid setting down how Peter died. Quite a while ago he confided to me he was distressed because he had had pain but had not passed a calculus. I should have seen what having been here over a year without producing a calculus was doing to his head. Somehow he decided he could vomit these calculi he believed had formed; so he got hold of some ipecac. Apparently he took the whole bottleful. He began vomiting early yesterday; at sunset when he hadn't stopped, though there was no longer anything to vomit up, Evelyn came and got me. I hadn't even known what he was going to do. He was very weak, but peaceful—so convinced of the rightness of what he was doing that I hesitated to interfere. So Evelyn and I sat with him, helping him when the nausea overcame him, bringing him water to moisten his mouth. The moon had canted down when we first noticed the blood. Less than an hour later he was hemorrhaging, waves of blood that spattered us, the walls, the bed, and he died soon after. Now it seems selfish somehow in the face of his death to have any feelings of my own about it: as if that represented a kind of annexation of his essence to my own. And yet all I could think to do when his body had lost all tone and began to take to itself that freight of dust all dead things—deer, dogs, fish—take up at the end; all I could think to do was to stand in the dark and scream at the valley and its safe fires: *Why doesn't anyone think about these things?*

And then later, the following correlations erected themselves in my head. I do not yet understand their significance, if any:

(A reduction formula)

GOLD = DISCIPLINED ASCETICISM (INWARD SHAPING)

$\updownarrow$

FREE CONTACT WITH COSMIC CHAOS (UNDERSTANDING ESSENTIAL CREATIVE/CHAOTIC CONFIGURATIONS) = GOLD?

(An expansion formula)

The Mountain Again:

It has been raining. Ruth, fulfilled, is on the opposite hillside, an abyss away. Peter is dead. The summer is gone. I am staying with Evelyn now. We live, we pass calculi of gold, we chink our shelters against the winter winds. The dogs, Sam, Emmett, and Ché, sniff the cooking pot after it has been licked clean, dreaming on the odors which reside in the metal, promising new sustenance. The stream is silted, rich. Ruth will bring her new baby and John to my shelter in the depth of the dozy winter; we will talk. I will be even more alone. I am trapped; trapped to pain and the gold calculi. Everything is very easy. I have been thinking again about the pile of gold in the abandoned cabin. Why did he abandon it? *He*, I say, coming to know him through his act. Because he understood it was a beginning, not an end? Do I really believe that? Gold—a beginning?

Or is it simply that he looked up at that enormous smile gashed into the mountain, and at the boulder-landslide premonitions which dribble from her lips moment by moment, now that the autumn rains are here?

In the book I borrowed from the child of this valley it is written:

FLY FROM THE WRATH TO COME

Instruction from Bly

Cynthia Macdonald

THE POET told me if I was serious
I must isolate myself for at least a year—
not become a hermit, but leave
my family, job, friends—so I did. My sister
agreed to take over as mother though not
as wife. I wonder if she will become that too;
I've always thought maybe she didn't marry
because she wanted Howard herself. So I
have moved here to North Dakota where
I work in a gas station, the only woman s.s.
attendant in N.D. Nowhere could be more isolated
and no job could: whistles and "Baby,
pump some of that to me" crack in the cold
or melt in the summer.

       try   try   try
    crycry   crycry   crycry   cry

I have been here seven months. Poetry should
be flowing from my navel by now, if . . .
Out of the solitude, I expected I would erect
something magnificent, the feminine analogue
of Jeffers' tower. Maybe it would have gone
into the ground instead of up.

s   k   y
                      high

I have discovered I drink when I am solitary. I
have discovered I can read page ninety-two of
Remembrance of Things Past twenty times in solitary
without ever reading it. If I don't die of alcoholism,
I will of cholesterol: solitary cooking.

  fryfryfry   fryfry   fryfryfryfry   frydie

Rhyme is important, my way of keeping
a grip on things. I wonder if the poet meant

it would all happen after I left, or if he is a sadist
who wants to send all those stupid enough to sit
at his feet to N.D. or S.D. or West Va.,
hazing before possible joining. I wonder if Jean
is in the double bed.

tower

power

I cannot think about the children, but I
do all the time. "Women artists fail
because they have babies." The last thing I wrote
was "The Children at the Beach" and that was over
a month ago. I am alone so I have to have company so
I turn on TV; at home
I only turned it off.

thumbtacks   processionals

north

red

It is time to go to work. First I need a drink. I consider
the Smirnoff bottle on the coffee table; a fly
lands on it. And then it all happens: the life
of that bottle flashes before me. Little by little,
or quickly, it is used up; empty, as clear as it was
full, it journeys to the dump; it rests upon the mounds of
beautiful excess where what we are—
sunflowers, grass, sand—
is joined to what we make—
cans, tires, and it itself in every form of bottle.
I put on my s.s. coveralls, a saffron robe, knowing I have
    found
what I was sent to find. The sky speaks to me; the sound
of the cars on Highway 2 is a song. Soon I will see the
    pumps,
those curved rectangles shaped like the U.S., and smell the
    gas,
our incense. O country, O moon, O stars,
O american rhyme is yours is mine is ours.

Hesse

Walter Abish

HESSE, PART ONE

WITHIN THE VACUUM rests another
vacuum, natch . . . and within Hesse
rests another Hesse, natch.
When I stepped into Hesse he was seventy,
I twenty-three. I experienced no discomfort,
only a mild sensation of levitation
and an urge
to further my career.

Are you Hesse too? he asked . . .
The sounds from the street below
seeped in through his nostrils.
It was pitch-dark inside. I may
strike a match, I remarked.
How does that strike you?

I am reconciled to death, he replied
in German. And within death
rests another death, natch.
Everywhere I go, kids read him.
They place him on the counter
face upward. The last time
in the Virgin Isles, but I
was too drunk to object,
and ridicule can be a premonition
of darkness.

HESSE, PART TWO

Absolutely no more tea. The Orient
has forsaken me. And so we stumbled
without a guide, and formed opinions
about the light. Apropos of light

there was a tree, we drank his health
and left at three. Fearing rain
we fingered the beads,
running back to commune with thee.
As habit has it our resources are low,
but within the low there rests a high,
natch.

The Day We Named Our Child
We Had Fish for Dinner

Michael Rossman

"What shall i do with the filet?" asked Karen from the kitchen. "There are bones in it."

"Cook it," I said.

"I don't like it with bones."

"They come out easier after it's cooked. That's the way fish are."

"Oh, never mind." Clatter of pans, water running. Indistinctly: "Screw you, anyway."

"What was that?"

"I said, never mind."

"And what else? What after that?"

Clatter of pans, running water. I pulled myself up again, weary, and went into the kitchen. She was standing over the stove, stirring instant mashed potatoes. I couldn't read her back. I held her. "I think we're tearing ourselves apart because the world is coming apart."

"I think you're right," she said.

"Water the plants," I told her, as I went back into the front room, grimly ignoring the radio, the phone. "That's the thing to remember now, remember to water the plants."

It was the fourth night of Cambodia. I was watching the ferns when our brother Lonnie from San Diego came in. "Carol called to find out when you're coming back," I reported. "She says they're working for a school-wide strike on Thursday. The English Department already voted to go out. Farber brought them round, and the paper's agreed to support it."

"All up and down Telegraph they're talking about Kent State," he said, his face still flushed from walking, intense through his spectacles. "There's little knots of freaks just talking, all along the street. It's true, four were killed, the

33

National Guard shot them down in the parking lots. I can't believe it."

We want to run a training program this summer, for public school teachers in the San Diego area: learn them a little political smarts to protect the learning they're learning. But Carol can't make the planning meeting, too busy with a crisis in the Woman Studies Program she's organizing in the college there. And she's hard to get hold of now: with the Minutemen at their door, they don't go back to the house much, and are learning to travel armed. Lonnie and I fumble to fix time for another meeting. Nothing will come into focus. He drifts out the door. I say, "Wait." We embrace.

Later Tom calls, from over in the next house, to tell me that Reagan has just ordered all the state colleges and universities closed through Sunday at least. Another first for California, the Golden State.

THREE YEARS BEFORE CAMBODIA I visited Kent, Ohio. Spring 1967. The media were just discovering the Haight and the Hippy. I was on my first round of visiting campuses, just starting to sort things out, to adjust my perspective from Berkeley-provincial to a national scope, and learn what work I could do in our ghetto. For the moment, I was writing a story on what the war was doing to what we then called the Student Movement, and I wanted some unknown dreary large public campus to play off against Antioch and Oberlin. So I chose Kent State, found a contact, and spent a couple of days there.

I mostly remember the flat apathy of the faces I met while on campus, these students of lower-class blood slack-weary from the mineral-drained hills of upland Ohio, many of them serving time for the upward mobility of the teaching credential. The buxom girls chattering in the morning Pancake House, as I sat over fourth coffee, road-grimed, hugging my sleeping bag.

Flat, that campus, flat. Some months earlier a first hiccup of antiwar protest had turned out a hundred for a lonely march. Now I found all told maybe a dozen committed to keeping active, trying to find a way to move it on. Isolated, embattled, embittered, taking refuge in an overtight group whose talk was laced with hurtful humor and flashes of longing.

They took me home for the night, the house was old and they had made their warm mark on its surfaces, they lived in what would become a commune, and then a family. Over late coffee we talked about organizing, about guerrilla theater, about holding together for warmth. Hang on, brothers and sisters, I said to them, some Spring is coming. And I left them the large *Yellow Submarine* poster I designed for Mario's birthday—an anarchist program for a disruptive festival of joy, "a generally loving retaliation against absurd attack." The poster commemorated the 1966 Second Strike at Berkeley—for us in the West, the first event in which freaks and politicos joined in public ritual, in song and an elaborate masque. We discussed community program, wild with the energy of coming together, and broke into spontaneous joy:

> *We all live in a yellow submarine,*
> *and our friends are all on board,*
> *many more of them live next door,*
> *sky of blue and sea of green. . . .*

Then next October, before I left to begin my second round of traveling campus work, we put on our feathers at dawn and marched 7,000 strong down into Oakland to block the doors of the Induction Center. After we got the shit clubbed out of 200 people, we tied up the downtown for the rest of the week, dodging the heat and chanting, "We are the people!" in the intersections.

So LONG AGO. *Saturday in Kent they trashed the town in protest, breaking 56 windows.* I was in Rock Island, Illinois, with my brother Russell from our theater troupe, talking about the death of a culture and teaching college kids how to begin to play again, to live in their bodies. *Sunday in Kent they burned down the Army ROTC building.* I was home in Berkeley, in the house we call Dragon's Eye. Sixteen of our family were learning to play a holy gambling game together, device for pooling psychic force, handed down from the Indians through Stewart Brand of the Pranksters. *Today in Kent on the fourth of Cambodia 2,000 turned out, and they shot 4 dead in the parking lots.* O let us laugh and canter. O I will play the Fool, grant me my mad anger, I still believe that art will see us through.

October evening falling in 1964. Berkeley. I was standing in Sproul Plaza beside the police car that held Jack Weinberg captive, I was changing in the crucible that formed the Free Speech Movement, the first campus explosion. It was the thirtieth hour since a thousand had captured the car and Mario stepped on top to begin the first open public dialogue I had heard in America. Behind Sproul Hall 600 cops were preparing, around us the Greeks were chanting drunkenly, "We want blood! We want blood!" We were sharing out green apples and bread, waiting for them to wade in clubbing, and singing "We are not afraid" in voices shaking with fear, betrayed into life by our longing for the pure radiations of community which we first there kindled among us, bright as imagination.

And I had a heavy flash, and said it to some friend: *"Five years from now they'll be killing kids on campuses, all over America."* They began with the blacks, with the Orangeburg Three massacred in '68, and they killed the first white brother, James Rector, at People's Park in Berkeley nine months later. And now Kent State: only the first in this, the fifth Spring.

(Rewriting now on the sixth of Cambodia, the plastic "underground" radio turns real as it tells me how the girl's leg broke as they beat her and threw her off the wall, an hour ago up on campus, and how 2,000 National Guardsmen have been ordered into Urbana, Illinois. I've spent ten separate weeks in Urbana, we have family there. Vic centers it, he works in wood and is making a cradle for the baby. Last month I saw him. He was organizing a craft-food-garage cooperative. The week before he had charged the pigs for the first time to help rescue a brother, was still shaken.)

But I had that flash and said that thing, I truly did, and have five years of poems to prove it, canceled stubs on the checking account of my sorrow, a long coming to terms. Sure, I'm a prophet, my name is Michael, I've shared total consciousness and seen the magicians summon the Powers. Prophets are common in Berkeley, and I've met quite a few on the road, mixed with the saints who now walk among us. What else do you expect to appear when our energy comes somewhat truly to focus?

IT IS TIME to own up to what we are doing. Everyone knows or suspects a snatch of the holy language of Energy, via acid, confrontation, or contact. The wavelengths of our common transformations flow strongly through Berkeley: for twelve years now, what happens here and across the Bay happens a year or two later in concentric circles spreading out across the young of America. I've lived here all that time. Most leave. If you stay, you close off or go mad. Or you stay open, and are transformed into an active conduit for the common sea of our Energy: lines of its organizing come to flow through you. I think I am learning to feel them in my body. It is frightening, it is always frightening not to have a language in which to wrap the nakedness of your experience. Cold wind of the new, hanging on the tip of the rushing wave.

For three years, linked into a growing net of comrades in work, I wandered from Berkeley through our involuntary ghetto. Four hundred days on the road, 150,000 miles. I visited seventy campuses, *worked* on forty, training and organizing, trying to follow the Tao of transformation in furthering the change that is happening through us. Call me an action sociologist, a specialist in learning and student of change; and color me proud to be supported mostly by my own people, freaks and radicals, plus some rip-offs from "adult" institutions and the media. I hustled to be free to put my energy where I draw my warmth, and luck was kind. And my trip is one among many. Our own and our best are staying with us now, instead of being bought off by the stale rewards of a dying System, and our change accelerates the more.

And I know where it's going, for a little way at least. For Berkeley is truly a barometer. Every college in the country is undergoing an evolution in the culture and politics of its captive transient population; and each evolution is essentially like Berkeley's. I have watched it happening on every kind of campus, from upper-class Catholic girls' schools to working-class junior colleges. Activism begins slow, diversifies to departmental organizing, antidraft work, and guerrilla theater; the dance of confrontation proceeds in growing ranks, the administration grows slicker but finally blows its cool; dope culture spreads, the girls chuck their bras—wow, you wouldn't believe the wealth of data.

And then beyond the campus the *voluntary* ghetto forms. Freak community sinks roots and begins to generate communes, families, head shops and food co-ops, freak media, friendly dog packs and dog shit, links with the farm communes—there are ten within fifteen miles of Rock Island, micro-sample of America. O, it is happening everywhere just like in Berkeley, only faster now: long-haired kids on the street, merchants' complaints, heavy dope busts, teachers fired, kids suspended, leash laws, narcs and agents and street sweeps and riot practice for the neighboring precincts, and dynamite at the farmhouse.

Here now in Berkeley it is the fourth night of Cambodia. Kent State is catching up fast. We shall have to go some to keep ahead. But like the University we have broad strength in our Departments, their lintels display the Tao of Life and Death. The Free Bakery has opened, capacity 2,000 loaves a day, put together by a family of forty living mostly on welfare: people drop by to pick up bread or learn how to bake, and linger. The city government is trying to get $175,000 for two helicopters to maintain a full-time patrol over the city; the City Council has decided not to make its meetings public, because of disruption; we will shoot their birds down, I am sure. A thousand tenants are out on rent strike; now the evictions begin. Governor Reagan is calling for a bloodbath. Gay Liberation flames buoyant in the front lines of demonstrations. Our medics are special targets, speed and smack are spreading like crazy. Six hundred Berkeley families are linked into the Great Food Conspiracy, buying cooperative spinach and cheese. The campus has the third-largest police force in the whole county, the leaves are beginning to wilt from the tear-gas. The people who hand-deliver the high-graphic newsletter *Kaliflower* to 150 communes in Berkeley and S.F., cycling goods and needs and lore and advice, come by and leave us a rap on planting and compost. My kid brother by blood was busted on campus last week, charged with assaulting a police officer with a deadly weapon, i.e., chucking a rock at a cop, $5,000 bail. He didn't do it, no matter: the Grand Jury's seeking indictments. The leaflet from the Berkeley Labor Gift Plan says, "*Together,* brothers and sisters, we can build a new community of labor and of love." Each time we go into the streets they test some new piece of technology upon us, last week it was cars spewing pepper-fog from their exhausts. The leaflet from the Leopold Family begs the community not to rip off records from the people's own store. On the radio a brother is reporting from Kent, he says he had to drive forty miles to get out from under the phone blank-out the government has clamped over the area. Berkeley was an exemplary city, you know. She had a progressive form of government and an overtly liberal party in power for years. She dazzled the nation with thoughtful, advanced programs of curricular enrichment and racial integration. Active support for the schools was her proudest civic tradition. O, Berkeley was always noted for how she cared for her children.

Cold wind coming. Sky turning black, the missiles sulk in their cages, the green net of the ocean grows dangerous thin, the terrorism of bombs begins, the Minutemen multiply bunkers, the economy chokes and staggers, the blacks grow yet more desperate, the War is coming home. I figure I'm likely to die in this decade, perhaps in this city I love, down the street beyond the neighborhood garden, in some warm summer twilight when people sit on their porches and the joy of live music drifts out from their windows. That's a cold political judgment, without much to do with what's also true: that since I woke at fifteen I've never been able to imagine past about thirty-five, it's been only a blank in my mind, always the same through the years, down to now, when I'm thirty. Do you mind if I finger my intimate fragments in front of you, awkwardly? I can't fit them together. But what else is a man to do in this mad time, pretend that everything's only at its usual standard of incoherence? For I have also been One with the great two-headed snake of the Universe, and I have seen us begin to recover our bodies and share our will, seen us learn that realities are collective conspiracies. Now in the families forming and linking we are weaving a blank social canvas for the play of our imagination. I have seen the first sketches of group will, love, and art, and a whole life, the first organized forms of human energy liberated one more degree. They transfix me with awe. I was never taught to dream so boldly, I had to learn for myself. I was not alone. For all our failures and unfinished business, what we are pulling together is bright and well begun. If we are let live through this decade and the next, we will be strong, strong, our women will be powerful and our men beautiful.

So ALL OF THIS is running through my mind on the fourth night of Cambodia, I'd just got back the night before from three months of hustling my ass around the country to pile up bread for the baby and the coming recession, in the process cutting through maybe sixty family groups in twenty cities, cross-fertilizing news and goods and paper and trinkets, a bee in the meadow of change. I came back stoned and mellow at how fast and strong it is coming together among us, even within the strain of the War, and bearing the love of a dozen fine women and men for Karen. All day now through the cottage people have been flooding with these atrocity tales, I wallow in the gloomy pleasures of verification. Diagnosis: Fascism, soft form turning hard, terminal cultural cancer. The radio tells me 258 campuses are out on strike, and then sings to me: "*Rejoice, rejoice, you have no choice.*" I take another toke, last of the good stuff: been running too fast to score, and summer's customary drought is almost upon us. The typewriter beckons. Torn between life and death I calm my chattering schizophrenic, refuse, and turn to the guitar, god damn! the sweet guitar who embraces all of me in her stroking vibrations when I touch her well. *O, how I need to go to the sea!*

Music is magical, music is my balm, music suspends me and aligns the frame of my spirit. O, shit, I wish I could sing to you, I am no longer ashamed, it is time to come out with it all, nothing less will do, the child will be born. I hate these pages, hate these mechanical fingers. Sometimes I pop for a moment above the surface of sanity and grab for the floating flute or guitar, manage to clear the Breath of my energy for a time from the choking hurrying flow of vital and desperate information, rapping words healing words data words analysis words magic words maggots and birds on the acid wallpaper of my mind. And I water the plants, the ferns in particular. When I am broken jagged like tonight I think it is because I mostly cannot cry, and that I travel the crystal rapids of melody for this reason too, singing because I cannot weep. When I'm together I see it as a way of keeping in touch with the slower rhythms. Either way the ferns are grateful, and they sing to me with their green misty love, and the spiders arch their webs in the corners of the window frames.

And I sing to them back, and to the dog my familiar, and to the pregnant animal Karen crouched unseen in her den—to them all, but softly to myself—a song I have made for her from a fragment another singer left in my mind. Karen comes in from the kitchen, plate and bowl of dinner in her hand, sets it down, retreats from the shaken animal in his den. While the rock cod cools, I sing the song again, for the first time loudly.

Slow, with a lagging rhythm

"Things might be
It   might be

la - zy   if   they weren't so   cra-zy,"___ he
bet - ter   in   some   o - ther   wea-ther,___ I

tells   you,   I   tell ___ you   that too.
don't   know, I'm   do - ing it   with you.

(2)

Some say the city, a farm would be pretty,
the mountains refuse to be blue.°
Come, with me wander, while they seek us yonder:
what else could you choose to do?

(3)

But pray for the baby whose birthday is Maybe,
and meet me at two in the moon.
Keep warm if you're able and fight for the cradle,
we can't hide, let's ride this one through.

Keep warm if you're able and fight for the cradle,
we can't hide, let's ride this one through.

"Now damn," I think, with bitter satisfaction, "ain't
that a song to inspire pity and awe and all! Not bad for a
first lullaby, opus 7. I sure would like to spend a long
stretch of years writing some songs. I'd be grateful if they
just kept on coming three or four a year, now that I know
they're coming." And I rack the guitar, pick up the plate,
and wander into the bedroom to eat with Karen.

IN THE NEXT ROOM my love is curled weeping on the
black leather chair, the dog is anxiously kissing her, careful
of her belly. I hold the song of her sobbing. "Ah, little
princess," I say, "you didn't know what it would cost to
be my muse." Through my head spin Cambodia, Babylon,
that five-year-old flash by the cop-car, growing up during

the McCarthy years with the FBI at the door, the times we have been in the street together, our trips, our campus travels. "But there's spin-off, you know," I say. "We're maybe better prepared spiritually for what's coming than most, advantage of foresight and practice, pay of the bruises. We've been making our peace for a while." No ultimate blame: culture changing too fast for its able. But the child will be born, though they tie the mother's legs.

"Yes," she says, "but I didn't know it would be this sudden." And then: "But if the gods are stingy with time, at least they've been generous in other ways."

On my lap. I see. Wavering. The plastic plate with pink decal flowers from the Goodwill. Fresh fish filet our cousin family brought us from up the Sonoma coast. Cheese sauce, recently mastered, with chopped green onions. Dehydrated mashed potatoes. In the stoneware bowls my sister Deborah made and laid on us for our anniversary—before she went down South again to the Army-base coffee shop she helped start, to watch her successors get six years and then go off to help organize another—in my dear blood sister's bowls is fresh spinach salad, well-flavored, we are learning to tend our bodies. Anticipation of apple juice in the refrigerator. This is how it is, you see, I am sitting here eating this food, and Bull is watching us very intently while the puppy from next door chews on his dinner, and my feet are up cuddled around the ball of her belly, watermelon-hard in its last weeks. I sing to her, we share the cooking, the dog eats when we do, mostly. She is bearing our child, on the bed under the light and the ferns is the government pamphlet on how to raise a child during the first year, it's not bad.

And she says, "What do you think of Lorca?"

"I think I can dig it, for a boy," I say slowly, "I been thinking about it, and I can."

"I'm glad," she says softly, the blush of shy triumphant pleasure crowning round her eyes. "Your mother and I were having lunch, and we started to think of the names of Spanish poets. 'García Rossman,' she said, 'no, that's impossible.' 'Federico . . .' I said. And then we just looked at each other, and we *knew*. And it has a nice sound."

I sink into the thought and mirror of her love, reach for the resonances, roots in the soil, and start to cry. Is it for the first time or the tenth, on this fourth night of Cambodia? Lorca was my first song teacher, the man who opened the keys of Metaphor to me: for ten years I relived his poems into my American language. "I have lost myself many times in the sea," he sang, "with my ear full of freshly cut flowers, with my tongue full of love and of agony. Many times I have lost myself in the sea, as I lose myself in the heart of certain children. . . ." Hold on, dear heart, jagged at this four A.M., now is not the time to tear. From Federico's arms I passed through those of grandfather Neruda, and then into Vallejo's volcano, which finished for me what acid began and gave me open form to integrate my fragments.

But Lorca began me, long before I learned how death found him in a Fascist trench, how he went to sleep forever in the autumn night of the gypsies, beyond the lemon moon. Mercurial brightest spirit of the second Golden Age of his tongue's power, murdered in Granada by Franco's highwaymen, in the first summer of the Civil War. All the poets, all, all the singers were on one side in that great division, perhaps as never before since old Athens. And the schools and the hospitals of the brief flowering of Republican Spain went down under German planes and Italian artillery, the dogs of Church and Greed. And all the poets perished or fled.

Torn, my father watched the Fascists rehearse, with their scientific grace; stayed to organize at home with his trade of words and a red perspective. I was born six months after the fall of Madrid, while he was editing the Mine, Mill and Smelter Workers' Union paper in Denver. Pablo Neruda was in exile from the Fascists in Chile. Cesár Vallejo was dead of hunger and heartbreak for Spain. Lorca's grave was never found, in a hundred lands and Franco's jails the poets of his race who survived sang him their tenderest elegies. Lincoln Steffens began a new family and life at sixty, his *Autobiography* instructed my father. When he died the last lines in his typewriter read, "the Spanish Civil War is the opening battle in mankind's struggle against Fascism." Steffens' son Peter taught my sister Deborah before she went South, I have touched his children. Even the high-school babysitters I hitched home from the airport with know what's coming down.

A WEEK BEFORE Cambodia I was at a conference in Boston, thrown by some church folk and book people, on "the religious dimension of the Movement." Indeed. It was quite a happening, believe me: a bunch of us freaks from the families got together behind some mellow mescaline and opened up some free space, some Chaos. Then someone asked about Ritual, and little incredible Raymond Mungo opened up in a musing country style, speaking the sainted baby babble.

"Well, we get up in the morning," he says, "and we look at the light and we eat, we eat together. And we go to sleep when it gets dark, sometimes alone and sometimes together, for there is no light. But sometimes at night we watch the moon. During the day we plant. We chop wood. We use the wood for fire. We eat when the sun goes down. From April to October there is very much food. We have to find ways to give it away. We have to, there is very much. There is the summer solstice, and then there is the autumn solstice, and so on. In spring the solstice was very cold, very cold. We chopped some wood and put it in a box. I made a mantra: *Equinox/sticks in box/soon it will be warm/big dog.* And a big dog came, and it grew warm. And sometimes we go out when there is no moon and run around in the grass. And then we come back to the houses we build. Last week one of our houses burned down, it was very warm. We lost four brothers and sisters. I think we're going to learn to build better chimneys."

O, I met a little saint in Boston, he organizes energy, used to be founding Czar of Liberation News Service, then he figured out the cities were dying, now in his Vermont town of 800, over a quarter live in communes, and he studies the government pamphlet to learn to build better chimneys. We're met on the fifteenth floor, overlooking the river of death called the Charles, the plastic pastries and draperies are poisoning our bodies, our minds, we've come to talk about rituals for living with fire. Mitch Goodman loves us and he's frantic with terror, sees the black sky looming, MIRV's lurking, etc., etc., he's positively yelling at Raymond, half his age and weight, scarecrow child in oversized coveralls: *"but what about Fascism?"* And somehow we can't quite get it through to him there that Raymond is not simply talking about farms, pigs, dinner, etc., but about the house burning down and learning to make better chimneys and going on in season, and about Lorca and Vallejo and my brother and my sister and two of each dead in Kent and my lover lazy with child, whose belly my baboon feet grip as if I stand on the round of the world, spinning through all time.

I was translating a poem of Lorca's when I got the call that my grandfather was suddenly dead. The poem follows a brief skit for puppet theater, in which the gypsy whose name is *Anything* is captured on the bridge of all the rivers while building a tower of candlelight, and is brought before the Lieutenant-Colonel of the Spanish Civil Guard to be interrogated.

He, Harry, my mother's father, was a Bolshevik. He organized a strike in the machine shop, was jailed, loved his tutor, she died of consumption, he fled here in 1906 to dodge the interrogations of the Czar, clerked and warehoused to send Mother through college. He wanted her to learn. I have his blue eyes. He taught me to carve, and cried with memory when I told him in '60, during that spring of Chessman and HUAC, how they beat us and hosed us down the steps of City Hall in San Francisco. "That was how it started, you know . . ." he said. And three years later the phone call came and was, and I put down the receiver and thought for a moment, and said somewhere inwardly and quite distinctly, I will file this for future reference, I will weep for you some day, grandfather. And I turned back to finish reworking the poem, for there was nothing to do but go on, I knew it would take years to comprehend that grief.

Sitting in my rocker, plate on my lap, our eyes intertwining and my feet on the future, the ferns turn to oleander and the cottage to a patio, and the song of the beaten gypsy rises up in the well of his absence.

Twenty-four slaps,
twenty-five slaps,
then at night my mother
will wrap me in silver paper.

Civil Guard of the roads,
give me a sip of water.
Water with fishes and boats.
Water, water, water.

Aii, boss of the Guard,
standing upstairs in your parlor!
There'll be no silk handkerchieves
to clean my face!

And the tears rip through me, Grandfather, deep, and out, everything opens and echoes in hers, and we touch and cling and are shaken. And the dog, our first child and familiar, pushes up anxious between us and offers her his nose and me his nads, which we take to complete the circle of energy, love, and time around the child to be born in Cambodia.

"Yes," I say, "Lorca, if it's a boy."

"Maybe even a girl," she says, "it has a nice sound."

"Maybe a girl," I say, "yes."

And she says I'm glad with her eyes.

And the radio sings, *"Rejoice, rejoice, you have no choice,"* and the acid magic of those moments, of that state we once called existential, goes on and on forever, and I go off to set down the brief notes of these thoughts, like the rib-thin eaten skeleton of the dinner fish, to flesh back out later. And then we take off for the City, to try to be with our people, our theater troupe in rehearsal coming suddenly real. For it is clearly a time for coming together with those we are dear with, and we must take care that the Wedding go on within the War.

The Gospel Bird

Frank Stanford

I SUPERMAN

Dressed in a superman suit
On the front porch of Chitum's store
I told all the Negroes "I can fly"
And jumped off the high end.

A German crop duster crashed.
A chicken ran out
And shit on a rusty three-penny nail,
Then ducked back under the stoop.

Blood and chickenshit
Dripping out of the hole
Into the good hand,
Jimmy says, "What you saving it for?"

He went to the fire
And nobody was studying me
But toad frogs and a dog.
"Whoa somebody! I done cut my hand off."

Nobody came but the Rollie Pollie man,
Skipping chuck-holes and swinging coal oil
In a copper-wired Co-cola bottle.
He says, "I'll tend to you boy, I'll tend to you."

II FIRE

Chitum's cripple nigger carpenter
Ate porch board bugs and did magic.
He had a police dog that brought him
Dead chickens in the night.

"Put hog lard on an oak tree,
Steal me whiskey and coal oil,
And this dog will bring your chicken back."
I wanted that bird.

"Lock Jaw and penicillin all the same,
Kill the chicken to kill the pain."
I got the nigger a fifth of gin
And he sent his dog after the bird.

The Rollie Pollie man told me how it was:
"The blood spurt out when that son-of-a-bitch
Chitum blew my crooked-necked
Chicken-killing dog in half.

"Black gnats was dying in the blood,
Some already drowned, I took coat wire
And drug him deep into the Diamond Woods."
My hand and Chitum's store burned that night.

III FLY AWAY, FLY AWAY

My father talked like he was singing
When he bought the burnt-out land and store,
But all I cared about was
The one thousand chickens in the deal.

He said to kill all the birds
And sell the meat to the levee camps
Up and down the river.
The Rollie Pollie man was on the run.

Jimmy was wringing their necks
And making a clean kill,
But I was knocking
Their heads off with a tomato stick.

Everytime I connected
I'd go check the bird out.
They'd bat their wings and squirt blood,
Winking at me.

I was busting green heads off ducks, too.
Jimmy had to hold me back.
"What's wrong with you, Superman?"
"Fly away, fly away, Gospel Bird," I cried.

Dont Talk to Me About War

Frances Starr

IN LAS VEGAS theres a Sunrise Hospital and a Sunset Cemetery The patient arrived at Sunrise in March and departed for Sunset in May Diagnosis cancer Location undetermined After thorough and prolonged examination the patient was too weak to be operable At first the patient was not informed it was cancer because it might impair her will to survive At last the patient was not informed it was terminal because it might depress her All necessary measures were taken to prolong the patients life and ensure her comfort

At periodic intervals surveillance and maintenance duties are performed Blood pressure pulse and temperature readings are taken At prescribed times the patient is made to swallow or be injected with recommended medication

The patient is cleaned at least twice daily All surfaces are swabbed The arms lifted legs and buttocks spread to get at protected areas The linen is changed at this time The bedridden patient is rolled first to one side then to the other Being too weak to move herself the patient is placed in a position other than the last to prevent bedsores The head of the bed is adjusted to a comfortable height A pillow is placed between the knees to alleviate discomfort from bone pressure

The patient is fed three times daily A soft diet is provided to encourage eating The patient has little appetite Few mouthfuls are coaxed into her Due either to the dehydration effects of oxygen or spread of the cancer to the throat or both eating appears to be painful

Intravenous feedings have been instituted The preparation consists of liquid vitamins in a glucose base The substance contained in a bottle suspended upside down over the patients bed feeds down a plastic tube at the end of which a hollow needle is attached A clamp on the tube regulates flow The needle is pushed through the skin into a vein and secured in place by gauze Nutrients in the sallow viscous fluid prolong existence

It was the dogs fault He crossed against the light The car screeched to a halt but nipped him in the rear and sent him skidding He regained his balance and kept on going a little unsteadily The next driver hit the brake hard but the cars momentum carried it forward hitting him broadside and throwing him a couple of yards Again he got to his feet and limping and yowling headed in panic for the sidewalk where he collapsed The SPCA took him away and put him to sleep

The patient hasnt the strength to attend to elimination A bedpan is provided for defecation Urination has been taken care of directly and automatically A hollow plastic tube is attached directly to the bladder and empties into a bedside container

Congestion builds up in the lungs making respiration difficult The fluid is extracted with a plunger device from which a needle protrudes The needle is stuck through the patients back and into the lungs The offensive substance is withdrawn by suction Extraction is an excruciating process The patient collapsed It may be necessary to perform it again

The patient suffers unbearable and constant pain This is alleviated through narcotics in liquid form The drug is contained in and administered through a glass tube with a plunger at one end and a needle at the other The skin is swabbed with antiseptic The needle pierces through the skin into a vein The plunger is pushed to inject the liquid The needle is extracted and the antiseptic swab is held over the hole to absorb the small amount of blood that seeps out Both arms are profuse with puncture marks Many are surrounded by black and blue patches The patient builds up an immunity and it is necessary to decrease the intervals between injections At this time it is necessary to administer the hypo every three hours The dosage is sufficient to induce sleep Periods of lucidity decrease

The patient attempted to crawl out of bed exclaiming Im dying Why dont you hit me over the head and get it over with It was necessary to physically and medicinally restrain her

The police were dragging the river beneath the pier A man middle-aged and rather drunk had tossed himself into the Hudson To his disappointment it was shallow enough to stand Ignoring shouts and directives from onlookers he threw himself face down in the water fighting it to stay there It would thrust him up and he would throw himself down again holding his head under determined to die They cast for him with a grappling iron They caught a fish The lead ball with protruding hooks was lowered on its chain again and again with ultimate success I saw him afterward He lay on his side as if in bed his right arm and leg straight the left ones bent His eyes were wide open His face was calm

The patient receives oxygen to facilitate breathing The congestion is such that is has been an almost constant necessity The oxygen comes from a central system built into the hospital walls with outlets above the bed The patient has been receiving it orally through a plastic tube with a mouthpiece similar to a narghile The effects of dehydration are evident The patients mouth is a round black hole the tongue and lips parched and discolored A nasal device has been substituted The oxygen feeds through a plastic tube surrounding the head into a hollow u-shaped piece that clamps onto the nostrils in the reverse manner eyeglasses pinch the bridge of the nose The skin around the nostrils has begun to crack as from the prolonged irritation of a running nose The nasal passages are drying out

Daily doses of cytoxin administered by injection have been replaced with the drug in pill form There has been no loss of hair or other violent reaction usually indicative of effectiveness

The intravenous needle must be extracted and reinserted elsewhere every few days The vein becomes saturated and seepage of the fluid into surrounding tissue enlarges portions of the anatomy as much as a third This is considered minor surgery and is performed by anesthetists The patient has lost a great deal of weight the veins are shrunken and withdrawn to harbor near the bone Various areas on the extremities are slapped in an attempt to enlarge and surface a vein The needle is unsuccessfully inserted several times before a receptive vein can be located Occasionally the probing needle hits a nerve head on and pain is felt despite the narcotic At present the needle protrudes from the patients thumb with some discomfort The patient frequently tries to extract it but hasnt the strength to lift her arm

I saw a death machine in a movie once a horrible invention of the Moslem mind From a platform two or three stories high an upended blade honed razor sharp descended like a sliding board to the ground The victim kneeled at the top A trigger device catapulted him forward and he fell to meet the blade severing himself in two as he slid It was over in seconds

The patients pulse is failing Digitalis is given to stimulate the heart

Earnest Remarks, Not Literature

Allen Wiggins

THERE IS no way to improperly begin
there is no way to begin
there is no way to imply form in the beginning
there is no way to palliate the ceremony

there is no way to undiscipline the genius
there is no way to flatten ripples from the
    thrown rock
there is no way to throw the rock to the bottom
there is no way to stop its drift to the bottom
there is no way to uncouple the truly married
there is no way to marry individuals
there is no way to individuate the ceremony
there is no way to begin kissing the bride
there is no way to stop kissing the individual

there is no way to achieve absolute being except
    quietly

there is no way to keep the revolution quiet
there is no way to keep the individual from
    kissing the revolution
there is no way to revolutionize kissing
there is no way to improperly begin the revolution
there is no way to discipline the revolutionary

there is no way to begin kissing the genius
there is no way to couple the genius
there is no way to individuate the revolution
there is no way to palliate the kiss
there is no way to achieve absolute ripples with
    palliatives
there is no way to conduct a ceremony of genius

there is no way to organize a mob
there is no way to kiss a mob

there is no way to stop a mob from acting in
    unison
there is no way to achieve absolute anarchy
    except with a mob
there is no way to achieve an absolute mob except
    with a leader
there is no way to keep the jocular faces in
    unison
there is no way to begin kissing the laughter
there is no way to scream the entire stanza

there is no way to begin disciplining the kissing
there is no way to keep the ending from having a
    beginning
there is no way to keep the marriage from being
    anarchic
there is no way to keep the marriage alive when
    one of the partners is not
there is no way to begin killing the partner
there is no way to begin parting the mob
there is no way to split asunder the joined
    revolution
there is no way to keep the revolution from
    being over
there is no way to achieve absolute ending except
    quietly

there is no way to keep words from affirming
there is no way to begin kissing words
there is no way to keep the sentence from
    beginning to form a kiss for its last word.

Richard Brautigan:
The Politics of Woodstock

John Clayton

I WANT TO TALK OUT my feelings about Richard Brautigan's *Trout Fishing in America*—about Brautigan's sense of life and about his politics. Because his politics are those of lots of my own people, maybe sometimes of my own life—and they disturb me.

Brautigan is talking (over a bottle of cheap wine that gets passed around) to the WE of a subculture—a subculture I'm a part of. He is creating for us a mental space called Trout Fishing in America where we can all live in freedom. He's not preaching about it to us: he assumes we're already there, or just about there. But I'm also in an unfree America, not by mental choice but by condition. And the politics of imagination is finally not enough for me. It's not enough for *us*.

In a chapter called "Sandbox Minus John Dillinger Equals What?" the narrator says,

> I let the baby play in the sandbox and I sat down on a bench and looked around. There was a beatnik sitting at the other end of the bench. He had his sleeping bag beside him and he was eating apple turnovers. He had a huge sack of apple turnovers and he was gobbling them down like a turkey. It was probably a more valid protest than picketing missile bases.

The politics of a baby in a sandbox and a sack of apple turnovers. It makes me mad—what would the peasants of Vietnam say about this kind of protest?—except that I also feel so close to his gentle mind I go along with his pastoral, a pastoral in the midst of death and dirt, hospitals and warehouses.

Until recently my knowledge about the Cleveland Wrecking Yard had come from a couple of friends who'd bought things there. One of them bought a huge window: the frame, glass and everything for just a few dollars. It was a fine-looking window.

Then he chopped a hole in the side of his house up on Potero Hill and put the window in. Now he has a panoramic view of the San Francisco County Hospital.

He can practically look right down into the wards and see old magazines eroded like the Grand Canyon from endless readings. He can practically hear the patients thinking about breakfast: *I hate milk,* and thinking about dinner: *I hate peas,* and then he can watch the hospital slowly drown at night, hopelessly entangled in huge bunches of brick seaweed.

He bought that window at the Cleveland Wrecking Yard.

The view I'm offered at the Cleveland Wrecking Yard's window is of bitterness and deadening brick. But Brautigan lets me out of dealing directly with that desperate reality (and I want to be let out); he snatches me up inside his *process of imagination*—the magazines eroding like the Grand Canyon, the magical perception of the patients' complaints. I am given imaginative magic as a liberation from decay.

Later in the same episode, the narrator goes himself to the Cleveland Wrecking Yard "to have a look at a used trout stream." He sees the sign:

USED TROUT STREAM FOR SALE.
MUST BE SEEN TO BE APPRECIATED.

Another writer might have produced an obvious satire on destruction and commercialization of the pastoral—a trout stream sold by the foot length. Of course the American trout stream has been sawed into pieces, animals extra. But this satire Brautigan soft-pedals: if the pastoral stream is no longer available, the pastoral of the imagination *is* available. I am seduced by his stoned imagination, which can *conceive of* a trout stream sold by the board foot; which can make a pastoral in a junkyard. What I am finally hooked by is the sensibility which can create a lyrical space in our heads by play, by metaphor.

BRAUTIGAN'S SENSIBILITY is personally liberating. It makes me happy by letting me feel my freedom. To the weight of this world he does not counterpose the *concept* of the imagination; he allows us to join him in his *process* of imaginative re-creation. *Imaginative re-creation* is not a fanciful critical term in talking about Brautigan; it is precise: The narrator's childhood friend becomes a "Kool-Aid Wino," doubling the water and pretending that the sugar is there—"He created his own Kool-Aid reality and was able to illuminate himself by it"; the narrator fishes in a creek "made narrow by little green trees that grew too close together. The creek was like 12,845 telephone booths in a row with high Victorian ceilings and all the doors taken off and all the backs of the booths knocked out." Or he turns the debris of a pauper's graveyard into a fishing fly:

Once, while cleaning the trout before I went home in the almost night, I had a vision of going over to the poor graveyard and gathering up grass and fruit jars and tin cans and markers and wilted flowers and bugs and weeds and clods and going home and putting a hook in the vise and tying a fly with all that stuff and then going outside and casting it up into the sky, watching it float over clouds and then into the evening star.

It is always a trout stream of the imagination that Brautigan fishes in. Like the stream the narrator as a boy creates out of a flight of stairs: "I ended up by being my own trout and eating the slice of bread myself." And even though Trout Fishing in America replies, "There was nothing I could do. I couldn't change a flight of stairs into a creek," we have already been part of exactly that magic transformation—and we are now presented with another: the transformation of a *topic* into a *character,* Trout Fishing in America, a character who signs a letter to the narrator with a wobbly signature; and into a book cover; and into the nickname of another character, Trout Fishing in America Shorty; and into a hotel; and into a gourmet: ". . . as if Trout Fishing in America were a rich gourmet and Trout Fishing in America had Maria Callas for a girl friend and they ate together on a marble table with beautiful candles."

Finally, it's a place: "I've come home from Trout Fishing in America, the highway bent its long smooth anchor about my neck and then stopped." It's a place of rambling, of freedom, of closeness with a peaceful, natural world. It's a place of winos in a park as well as of actual fishermen. And if it's disappearing in a reality of institutionalized campgrounds with flush toilets, it remains alive in Brautigan's way of seeing. Salvation through perception: the politics of inner freedom.

The mental space we enter with Brautigan's narrator is shaped by an attitude toward language, by tone, and by narrative structure as well as by metaphor. It is a political space in that it reinforces "our" values—the values of a subculture that sees itself as flipped outside of goal-oriented, psychically and socially repressive, exploitative, aggrandizing American technological society. It is political in that to go into that space is to decide *not* to confront that other society.

I want to define this mental space by talking about the beautiful chapter "Sea Sea Rider." The episode begins:

> The man who owned the bookstore was not magic. He was not a three-legged crow on the dandelion side of the mountain.
> He was, of course, a Jew, a retired merchant seaman who had been torpedoed in the North Atlantic and floated there day after day until death did not want him. He had a young wife, a heart attack, a Volkswagen and a home in Marin County. He liked the works of George Orwell, Richard Aldington and Edmund Wilson.

The man was not magic. Who said he was? What do you mean, *magic?* What is a three-legged crow and why would it find its way to the dandelion side of the mountain? Why *of course* a Jew? Why put into series facts that so obviously don't belong together? It is not just that Brautigan's narrator is illogical; surreal connections between images is part of his stance. He invites me to share these connections with him—assumes I am following completely. Of *course* you can buy a trout stream in pieces; of *course* Trout Fishing in America is a character who can remember "with particular amusement, people with three-cornered hats fishing in the dawn."

He [the bookstore owner] learned about life at sixteen, first from Dostoyevsky and then from the whores of New Orleans.

The bookstore was a parking lot for used graveyards. Thousands of graveyards were parked in rows like cars. Most of the books were out of print, and no one wanted to read them anymore and the people who had read the books had died or forgotten about them, but through the organic process of music the books had become virgins again. They wore their ancient copyrights like new maidenheads.

I went to the bookstore in the afternoons after I got off work, during that terrible year of 1959.

What is important is not that Brautigan uses a wildly fanciful metaphor but that he expands it into an image and then blurs one metaphor (books: graveyards) into another (graveyard: cars) into another (books: virgins). The man may not be magic, but I am captured by a magical process in the writing.

Part of the magic is in the discontinuity itself. If *Trout Fishing in America* is in part a life-style of freedom and rambling, these qualities are present not only in the metaphorical transformations and illogical connections but in the apparent looseness, casualness, easy rambling of the narrator's talk. It isn't true that the parts of *Trout Fishing in America* could be shuffled at random—some, for instance, are necessary preconditions for others to make sense; but we are intended to *feel* that there is absolutely no ordering. And within a chapter Brautigan creates the stance of careless rambler just as Arlo Guthrie does in the record of *Alice's Restaurant.* In "The Cleveland Wrecking Yard," for example, Brautigan begins with the experience of his friends, talks about the mansion of a dead actor, then about two Negro boys discussing a champion twister—all before he gets to the story of his adventure with the trout stream in the wrecking yard.

In "Sea Sea Rider" the narrator tells us that one day when he was sitting reading about Billy the Kid,

The owner of the bookstore came up to me, and put his arm on my shoulder and said, "Would you like to get laid?" His voice was very kind.

"No," I said.

"You're wrong," he said, and then without saying anything else, he went out in front of the bookstore, and stopped a pair of total strangers, a man and a woman. He talked to them for a few moments. I couldn't hear what he was saying. He pointed at me in the bookstore. The woman nodded her head and then the man nodded his head.

The narrator doesn't want to—but the girl convinces him:

When I came out of the bathroom, the woman was lying naked on the couch, and the man was sitting in a chair with his hat on his lap.

"Don't worry about him," the girl said. "These things make no difference to him. He's rich. He has 3,859 Rolls-Royces." The girl was very pretty and her body was like a clear mountain river of skin and muscle flowing over rocks of bone and hidden nerves.

"Come to me," she said. "And come inside me for we are Aquarius and I love you."

I looked at the man sitting in the chair. He was not smiling and he did not look sad.

I took off my shoes and all my clothes. The man did not say a word.

The girl's body moved ever so slightly from side to side.

There was nothing else I could do for my body was like birds sitting on a telephone wire strung out down the world, clouds tossing the wires carefully.

I laid the girl.

It was like the eternal 59th second when it becomes a minute and then looks kind of sheepish.

"Good," the girl said, and kissed me on the face.

Afterwards the bookstore owner tells the narrator "what happened up there." And he tells two stories built on literary clichés. The first is about lovers in the Spanish Civil War; the second is about a wild Western hero who rides into Mexico, where the *rurales* are terrified by his gun and his sexual habits:

"You became the most powerful man in town.

"You were seduced by a thirteen-year-old girl, and you and she lived together in an adobe hut, and practically all you did was make love.

"She was slender and had long dark hair. You made love standing, sitting, lying on the dirt floor with pigs and chickens around you. The walls, the floor and even the roof of the hut were coated with your sperm and her come.

"You slept on the floor at night and used your sperm for a pillow and her come for a blanket.

"The people in the town were so afraid of you that they could do nothing.

"After awhile she started going around town without any clothes on, and the people of the town said that it was not a good thing, and when both of you began making love on the back of your horse in the middle of the zócalo, the people of the town became so afraid that they abandoned the town. It's been abandoned ever since.

"People won't live there.

"Neither of you lived to be twenty-one. It was not necessary.

"See, I do know what happened upstairs," he said. He smiled at me kindly. His eyes were like the shoelaces of a harpsichord.

I thought about what happened upstairs.

"You know what I say is the truth," he said. "For you saw it with your own eyes and traveled it with your own body. Finish the book you were reading before you were interrupted. I'm glad you got laid."

Once resumed, the pages of the book began to speed up and turn faster and faster until they were spinning like wheels in the sea.

The bookstore owner is a kind of guru, even if he's not magic. He teaches the life of the imagination to a strung-out, life-denying young man. To get laid is simple, as in "once upon a time." But it is also wildly fantastic: experience is maybe always literary, symbolic, metaphorical. Certainly it makes more sense to see events in terms of the fantasies implied in them than as "objective" facts (indeed, isn't objectivity only one more, less adequate metaphorical perception?). The narrator has learned the bookstore owner's truth, and returns to his reading in a different manner—". . . the pages of the book began to speed up and turn faster and faster until they were spinning like wheels in the sea."

THIS PASSAGE does wonderful things to my head. I feel the freedom, the openness, of the narrator's trip. He becomes a Sea Rider. I remember the song—sometimes called "See, See, Rider" or "Easy Rider"—from which the chapter title comes. It's a blues about rejection after love-making. But the problem of that blues is gone; getting laid is easy; the narrator becomes a Sea Rider, spinning his fantasies like wheels in the sea.

Early in the chapter the narrator explains, "I went to the bookstore in the afternoons after I got off work, during that terrible year of 1959." The rich man has 3,859 Rolls-Royces. Making love was like the eternal 59th second. All incomplete, waiting numbers. But at the end of the episode, the pages spin. The anticipation of climax is over, somehow. Things just go on. They go on unexpectedly and are gifts, like the afternoon love-making.

What the bookstore-owner-teacher does for the narrator, Brautigan's style does for me: his simple narratives, his synapses of logic, his assumption that we will of course accept what he says without asking for explanations, his rambling structure, his metaphorical shifts, his gentle pastoral imagery. We are become as little children, just as the listeners to Jesus' parables must have been as much transformed by the simple diction and syntax and childlike transitions as by the stories themselves. Sometimes Brautigan actually *describes* a way of life:

> Pard and his girl friend sleep in the cabin and the baby sleeps in the basement, and we sleep outside, under the apple tree, waking at dawn to stare out across San Francisco Bay and then we go back to sleep again and wake once more, this time for a very strange thing to happen, and then we go back to sleep after it has happened, and wake at sunrise to stare out across the bay.

But it's not the description—it's my sharing, our sharing, in Brautigan's imaginative process that really does such beautiful things to us.

> Unit 4 had a big wooden table with benches attached to it like a pair of those old Benjamin Franklin glasses, the ones with those funny square lenses. I sat down on the left lens, facing the Sawtooth Mountains. Like astigmatism, I made myself at home.

The association with early America, the connection with the mountains, the simile becoming fantasy: I am also made to feel at home. Brautigan's style says I can discard categorized living, since *his* perceptions are free to bounce in and out of categories at will. It says I can discard consciousness of causality and rational connections. "But the thing that smelled the most like sheep was the very sun itself. When the sun went behind a cloud, the smell of the sheep decreased, like standing on some old guy's hearing aid, and when the sun came back again, the smell of the sheep was loud, like a clap of thunder inside a cup of coffee." The style says I can ignore moral dicta, says this by its acceptance of people and events without even asking whether they should be accepted. Things simply *are*. And underlying this sense of life are gentleness and mental freedom.

Brautigan's style undercuts the long tradition of realistic fiction. *Trout Fishing in America* is not an anti-novel; it is an un-novel. Brautigan has no interest in character—in introspection or psychological insight, in interpersonal dynamics; no interest in materiality; no interest in time or causality. The book runs profoundly counter to the bourgeois instincts of the novel. It runs counter to the bourgeois world view of practicality, functionality, rationality. But it isn't a rebellious, individualistic book. Not at all. There is *no* rebellion in it. It accepts everything, even the world that is destroying the pastoral possibilities it asserts. And even though the chapters are often solitary adventures, it is still the book of a subculture, of a WE who are so different from bourgeois expectations as not to need explanations about our way of life.

I am not arguing—not at all—that Brautigan *denies* death and suffering. They are very necessary parts of the book. The bookstore owner floated on the Atlantic till "death did not want him." Again and again death and suffering are connected with beauty. That is the point—that Brautigan *transmutes* ugliness and sadness. Like the ex-errand boy for an abortionist and the ex-hustler who live together in a room in Hotel Trout Fishing in America: the room is the same imaginative place that the narrator finds in the woods or in the cabin across San Francisco Bay. It is a human, kindly place. But it exists in relation to the past of illegal abortion and prostitution and in relation to death: her ex-pimp wants to kill the man, and so he sleeps with a .32 pistol by their bed. Their cat, 208, is named after the room number of the bail office—a remembrance of bad times. But they've made it: "They had a good world going for them."

Or look at the episode "Worsewick": a playful pastoral which contains elements of death as matters of simple fact. Brautigan doesn't solemnize or moralize death; it is just *there*.

The narrator in "Worsewick" describes bathing with his woman in a not-too-fancy hot springs.

> There was a green slime growing around the edges of the tub and there were dozens of dead fish floating in our bath. Their bodies had been turned white by death, like frost on iron doors. Their eyes were large and stiff.

In the slimy water they make love:

> Then I came, and just cleared her in a split second like an airplane in the movies, pulling out of a nose dive and sailing over the roof of a school.
> My sperm came out into the water, unaccustomed to the light, and instantly it became a misty, stringy kind of thing and swirled out like a falling star, and I saw a dead fish come forward and float into my sperm, bending it in the middle. His eyes were stiff like iron.

The voice says that everything is cool. When a writer like Hemingway connects love and death it is to counter love with death and death with love. For Brautigan they are both *okay*.

THE STYLE OF *Trout Fishing in America* sucks us into the politics of no politics—the politics of a subculture alive in *another place*. For Brautigan, America itself is "often only a place in the mind." Unfortunately, however, America is real. Fred Hampton was murdered in his bed by the police. Their bullets did not become trout or sperm nor the guns surrealistic pillows. B-52's are every day dropping 3,000-pound bombs and CBU's—anti-personnel shrapnel bombs aimed at wiping out all Vietnamese not under concentration-camp control. Brautigan can get away with his freedom by living mentally in the interstices of the manipulative social structure and by ignoring both imperialism and racism. He is not alone there. Brautigan has been taken up as a tribal hero, along with the plain-folks Mister Dylan of "Country Pie" and the pastoral evocations of the uncomplicated South (The Band, Creedence Clearwater Revival). He is part of what's been called the Woodstock Nation, living, as one friend said about herself yesterday, as if "our" revolution had already happened. All right. We simplify our lives and try to pass them in inner quiet and mutual respect. A week ago after a day of housebuilding, I went swimming with friends in a nearby pond. Three young people were already at the pond. We didn't know them, but from their faces and clothes we understood that they were our people. We talked about where we lived in the area, and discovered mutual friends. We were all in the Other Place. The Woodstock Nation, the tribes. Until the local police chief came to kick us out: "Around here we expect people to behave themselves," he said. The America of institutions has always known how to handle Indians: exterminate the rebels, herd the rest into reservations to live on organic foods and organic mescaline, commercialize then idealize their culture once it's no longer a threat.

I don't want to live on a reservation. I, and many of my friends and students, having been very excited by Richard Brautigan, have begun to see *why* he's been so much a cult hero: like the Beatles, he gives people the assurance that they can be free and part of a community of free people, *now.*

About a year ago, Ray Mungo published in a commune magazine an essay that spells out the politics of a major portion of the Woodstock Nation:

> You are an independent state. If you want peace . . . find it in your heart. Form a domestic and foreign policy. Find clever ways to keep the Suez Canal open unless and until you can provide all your needs independently of anybody else. . . . Don't exploit your brother 'cause it ain't nice and anyway Johnson & the USA have already proved it won't work. . . .

What your underdeveloped country needs is a little corner to be warm, some great books to read and write, good grains and fresh meat and whole milk to feed yourself, unlimited access to music and painting supplies (hey, did you know there is free music in the spheres, not to mention the public libraries?), and loads of love. And fresh air and room to roam.

Richard Brautigan's version of that country is called "ideath" and its chief raw material is Watermelon Sugar. So Brautigan is even further into another place than Ray Mungo. A place of the spirit. But I am suspicious of a revolution of the spirit that turns its back on a revolution against the institutions of death.

I wonder: is it possible to have both Brautigan's revolution and Che's? To change society requires some share of those same qualities that Brautigan's style denies: causality, goal orientation, and outrage. We have to look at the debris of American cities and be angry. We have to respond with *reasonable fury* to the attempts by the ruling class to manipulate us and to control the rest of the world. We must be organized and move toward the goal of a life-nourishing society, while Brautigan's style conveys a peaceful, humorous response which seems to transcend present evil.

The cover of *Trout Fishing in America* is important. It shows a young couple in front of the statue of Benjamin Franklin in San Francisco's Washington Square. The girl is dressed in a long skirt, high boots, wire-rimmed glasses, and a lace hair band; the man is wearing a nineteenth-century hat, a vest and black coat over his paisley shirt and beads. He too has wire-rimmed glasses. With his vest and glasses, with her boots and lace, they look like something out of an earlier America. They reflect the nostalgia which permeates this book: for a simpler, more human, pre-industrial America. Brautigan knows it's gone. But some of the values in this book are derived from this kind of nostalgia. Brautigan has created a pastoral locked in the past, a pastoral which cannot be a viable social future.

I want to live in the liberated mental space that Brautigan creates. I am aware, however, of the institutions that make it difficult for me to live there and that make it impossible for most people in the world. Brautigan's value is in giving us a pastoral vision which can water our spirits as we struggle—the happy knowledge that there is another place to breathe in; his danger, and the danger of the style of youth culture generally, is that we will forget the struggle.

FIVE POEMS

William Matthews

Ball and Chain, Yes Indeed

> *It's all feeling.*
> *—Janis Joplin*

DEATH'S BREAD is still rising.
So much for food.
It's bad enough that
my breath is spliced
to the breath of the dead.
A barge of perfect garbage
arrives for re-cycling.
I hate this: I'm going to give
your gift away.
I hope I don't love
whoever's next.
I can feel the braid of my breath
fray. I'll ruin my voice
with this warning.
Cut me loose, I love you
too much.

Hard Stuff

YOU KNOW the way they say "on drugs,"
the dilettantes?
You learn one
well, that prickle
the lines in your palms make
retracting, pulling
the little fat that's left
over them for the night.
There's no plural. The hands
hate one another.

Night Driving

You FOLLOW into their dark tips
those two skewed tunnels of light.
Ahead of you, they seem to meet.
When you blink, it is the future.

Suppose

THE FUTURE isn't out there
waiting,
nor is the past snail-slime
(like Heisenberg's particle
it is deflected
by the light we see it by).

And sperm survive so long
an unfaithful woman
sometimes carries home
dead letters still alive,
foxfire, broken code.

Or, "Time
like a pacing coach
frets the field away."
Suppose the universe
is running down, a clockful
of dying crickets.
Downward to darkness on extended
metaphor.
In the History of Ideas
everything Good is Done For.

Yet

light like a stream
of liquid beads
drills into open eyes
across a space its flowing
strings.
　　　　To blink implies
muscular faith:

there isn't time for much
to change
　　　　and
blood loops like a tape
recording of great prayers
about the blood,
about the blood.

Sleep

Last cough,
lungcells six hours safe from cigarettes.
The testicles drone
in their hammocks
making sperm.
Glut and waste
and then the beach invasion,
people
everywhere, the earth in its regular
whirl slurring to silence
like a record at the onset
of a power failure.
I'm burning ferns to heat my house.
I am
the Population Bomb, no,
not a thing but a process:
fire: fire.

Ashes and seeds.
Now in my drowse I want to spend,
spend before the end.

Sleep with a snowflake,
wake with a wet wife.
This is the dream in which the word "pride"
appears as a comet.
Its tail is the whole language
you tried as a child to learn.

Difficult and flashy dreams!
But they're all
allegory, like that corny comet.
You can turn your head fast
and make the light smear,
and you wake to watch it
staining the windows, good
stunned morning, people
everywhere, all of us
unraveling, it's so good
to be alive.

Dare to Struggle,
Dare to Win

James Kempton

WAITING FOR THE MEETING to begin we are restless. Why are we having this meeting? Nothing's happened that we need a meeting for. We have too many meetings. The chairman says the room is crowded and people will have to stop smoking. We open the windows. Those by the windows are cold. They shut them. Soon it is too smoky. The windows are opened again.

There is a motion on the floor. Rules of order only interrupt free flow. Free flow is always circular. We are getting nowhere. The usual speakers. We stop listening and whisper. The group is too large. Every night the same divisions. We are tired of each other and confused. Words mean nothing.

Jill reviews the situation:

1. We took this building because we all felt the need to act.
2. This group is the product of that collective action.
3. The next move is theirs.
4. They know this but do nothing.
5. They are waiting for us to make a mistake.
6. The nature of our response is in doubt.

With silence, difficulties grow vague. We touch each other softly. Someone begins a story. It is long and personal, but we do not want it to end. We are taking off our clothes. Annie shows us what she has woven during the

73

meeting. We admire tangible progress. Bill does his imitation of Big Cheese. It is late, but everybody feels too excited to sleep. We are together.

ANNIE USED TO BE A VENTRILOQUIST:

SHE HAD A DUMMY named Petey the Penguin and she worked on a TV show in Boston called *Mother Goose Time*. She said it was dull but they paid her all right. The trouble started when she got sick. The station manager called up every morning to ask how Petey felt. All the kids sent Petey cards. Nobody gave a damn about her. Annie was jealous. She and Petey used to lie in bed all day fighting. By the time they went back to work, Petey had turned into a smartass. She could never tell what he was going to say. One day he called Mother Goose a Honky, on the air. After she was fired, Annie went to the Welfare Department with Petey wrapped up in a blanket and said she was an abandoned mother. They gave her money. But Petey started screaming all the time. It drove her crazy, she couldn't get any sleep. Then the Welfare tried to make her put Petey up for adoption. Annie dropped him down an air shaft and left town.

BROTHERS AND SISTERS:

THIS IS THE 32nd day of our struggle. We continue to think of the brave miners of Ulali who for 32 days lay trapped under 700,000 tons of coal, refusing to cooperate with rescue parties until the owners met their demands. Every day wives and children gathered at the pit head and begged them to come out. Reporters promised to take their pictures. The bosses offered them fringe benefits and sliding wage scales. The miners answered: "This is the People's coal. It cannot crush us!" Where are the miners of Ulali now? They are in this room! They give us strength!!

THE LEADERSHIP:

"I THINK THE LEADERSHIP is getting depressed," said Annie. "Pretty soon we'll have to appoint a new bunch. Whose turn is it?"

Bill has been nominated but declines on principle:

"What do we need a leadership for? To keep track of how long we've been in here? It doesn't matter to me. Time was invented by the bosses to bust you for being late to work. Ask the miners of Ulali. To negotiate our demands? Personally, I wouldn't take our demands to a dog fight. Of course, Big Cheese rejects them. To put out position papers, press releases, ultimatums, and bulletins? Writing is elitist bullshit. The leadership, being another piece of elitist bullshit, naturally goes in for it."

The Army gave Bill a test once. The correct answers were arranged in random order. Bill's answers were also in random order. But nowhere did the pattern of his answers match the correct pattern for the test. When the Army told him, Bill was not surprised.

FACTS:

BIG CHEESE, Bill said, is making up his annual report:

Today, we occupy 450,000 square feet and we are still expanding . . . in Communications, Countermeasures (Active & Passive), Counter-countermeasures, and Automatic Test and Check-out Systems.

"Big Cheese," said Nancy, "is married to the daughter of an underwear king. They live in a garden apartment with their six children named Brook, Kurt, Bart, Hope, Sage, and Hollister. He calls them 'team.'"

"The doorman is always having trouble with his car," Sam said, "but Big Cheese knows an excellent mechanic."

"Big Cheese," said Jill, "has the memory of a Russian. He thinks in diagrams. When he laughs, it sounds like a toilet flushing in the next room."

"Big Cheese goes to the movies a lot," said Susan. "Last night he saw one with Charlton Heston, Richard Widmark, and Burt Lancaster. It was about the space plague."

"Big Cheese," Bruce said, "wears shiny green suits. He cops feels in elevators. His farts are silent but deadly."

"Big Cheese," said Annie, "is brains in brown butter."

We know he grows by circular secretion. Facts collect along his folds.

JILL SAYS SHE IS PREGNANT:

"THIS KIND OF THING has happened before and I know how to deal with it. Still, it sets me thinking.

"First of all, the sex around here stinks.

"In the second place, there is entirely too much crick-pricked ideology. Last week the brothers threw out Big Cheese's deep-pile rug because it was a symbol of privilege. If they want to know about privilege, let them ask the sisters who are on the bottom getting splinters by the ass-ful.

"Thirdly, the division of labor here has fallen into the usual pattern: Men shave, smoke, and make speeches. Women clean, cook, and take notes.

"Fourth, experience has shown that a sexually integrated discussion of this subject is a waste of time.

"Therefore, I am announcing the formation of a Women's Independent Caucus, which will take the necessary steps."

SAM TELLS US A STORY:

HE AND A FRIEND were sitting in a bar one night when a woman came up and asked them if they wanted to make five dollars apiece for a few minutes' work. They said sure and went over to her place. She had a crate of oranges she wanted them to throw at her. She took off her clothes and stood near the wall. Sam and his friend were a little nervous, but they started to lob the oranges. Harder, she kept yelling. Pretty soon, Sam said, they got into it. They began yelling too. They threw so hard their arms got sore. The woman was covered with big welts and shivering all over, then she came. After she had paid them, Sam and his friend stayed to help her clean up.

Jill wanted to know if that was supposed to be a happy ending.

Bruce says that Sam made the whole thing up just to get her mad.

A MESSAGE FROM BIG CHEESE:

MEN & WOMEN:

I regret to inform you that your demands are obsolete.

If you want to rejoin us, we stand, as always, oiled and ready. Otherwise, the structure you occupy can be easily detached and flown to a waste area.

Yours,

B. C.

TACTICS

NANCY OBJECTS to Big Cheese's tone. She suggests that we burn the building down to teach him a lesson. Nancy set off her father's store during civil disorders last spring and found this effective. At least, she says, it would get us back on the street and save face.

Jill doubts that Big Cheese learns lessons. She agrees that it is time to leave but maintains burning the building would not achieve our political objectives. To expose the coercive and cynical nature of the authority Big Cheese represents, we must make him evict us by force. In court we can raise larger issues that challenge the legitimacy of the legal system. When we lose, we can define our commitment in the face of repression by going to jail. Then we use the hypocrisy and brutality of prison to educate and organize the inmates.

Bruce suspects that Jill has never been to jail or she wouldn't talk that way. He says jail isn't so bad, as long as you don't worry about justice. The last time, Bruce was arrested for hitchhiking in a bear suit. They sent him to the hospital for observation. He bit a doctor and they put him back in the joint. Bruce says it doesn't matter where you are. Institutions are all alike. There's not much work and lots of drugs and sex to pass the time.

Susan thinks that when the police come we should take off our clothes, which will freak them out and they won't know what to do.

Annie says they will know exactly what to do.

Sam wants to kidnap Big Cheese instead and cut off pieces of him until they agree to our demands.

But, according to Bill, they couldn't agree to our demands even if they wanted to. That's the whole point of our demands. We're not here to negotiate, we're here to win.

LAST NIGHT SUSAN DREAMT A DREAM:

WE WERE LYING AROUND the way we usually do, when suddenly we realized we had won. Nobody spoke. Everything was just clearer. We were happy and we knew why. We looked out the window. A crowd was starting to form. We had to hurry. We took our posters off the walls and rolled them up. We swept the floors. There wasn't time to write a statement. We went outside. The television lights came on. We stood in a long row. The lights made our eyes water. All the people wore armbands in honor of us. They had brought trays of little sandwiches and mints. We passed them down the row. The crowd was cheering. We were quiet. Then they went away. There was a full moon. We ran around in the grass and everybody fucked.

"Who did you fuck?" Sam asked.

"Big Cheese. He wasn't bad for an old guy."

"Susan," said Jill, "you will never learn."

Karate

Stanley Plumly

If I could chop wood,
if I could just cut through
this furniture,

the paraphernalia
of blocks
and stacks of boards,
wedged and
piled
head-high,

if I could break the back
of a single two-by-four,

if the Japanese instructor would only
lay his little building
of bricks
in front of me,

if I could only drive nails
deep into the hard rose of the wood.

A Good Revolution

Paul Spike

"The pleasure is mine," said Billy. He was squatting on his muscular haunches in short shorts and white sweat socks. The cries of the Ecoy bird were shrill. Billy had just shown TxuTxu, the local witch doctor, how to put on a Band-Aid. TxuTxu smiled through the gaps in his yellowed teeth and sang out into the jungle, "Optre gom buckni ti ti chi!"

The drums throbbed back an answer.

Billy had been here in West Lhoopville for seventeen months as a member of the Helping Hand of Jesus, a missionary outfit which specialized in young fellows just out of seminary who wanted to "see the world" a bit before settling down in some local parish. Billy had made good progress with his tribe. They were former vegetarians who had become meat eaters back in the twenties when the Catholic wave passed through the land. Billy was the first "ti ti chi" they had seen in over thirty years. His first task was to make them natural again, bring them back to the old vegetarian dietary laws.

Lois was the nurse on Billy's team. She was from Rye, New York, and tall, with one side of her face showing some giant strawberry pimples.

Dowler F. Rene leaned back in his leather chair and leafed through the report. It was a classified piece on student coalitions with the Epileptic Movement and especially the dealings of a terrorist outfit called the Helping Hand of Jesus. Miss Darlington came strutting into his office.

"Yes, Betty?"

"The moustache wax you ordered from Uruguay, sir. Here," she said, and dropped the thin zinc tube on a pile of security clearances.

"Thanks, Betty." He grinned thinly, a cloud of cut weed floating over the Normandy graves, his guts turning in slow twists.

Dowler Rene was a trustee of EAT: Exterminate All Trouble. He thrived on climax and academic freedom; crisis was his second nature . . . nailed to the floor of his federal garage forty stories beneath his latest white paper. Betty pulled at his electric sucker; it had fastened itself to her pink belly. The latest device from Research and Development, the hearing aid had a fetish for secretarial flesh. She turned and yanked it off her and then pumped three anxiety darts into the trustee. He was beginning to ooze yellow smoke as she dialed the Helping Hand of Jesus Regional Office.

"This is Betty at EAT, copy copy over . . ."

"We copy . . ."

"Have walrus uptight. Expect trustee patrol any second. Can you locate red tape? Send bandage, smokes, and anti-sucker ointment."

"Betty?"

"What?" she asked impatiently.

"We just occupied Wheeling, West Virginia!"

"Beautiful, man . . ."

Billy saw Lois in her bra and panties standing in the stream. The bushes were very dense there and filled with the fiery TiTi bugs. The brown water reached up to the middle of her thighs. He saw where it was dark beneath her panties, where the black inky hairs were resting in little coils. He looked at her bra for a sign of her nipples but either they were not erect or it was one of those thick bras. He kept wondering if she would take off her clothes and bathe her naked body. That would be foolish, he thought, since this water stains so terribly. Why isn't Lois at the hospital?

"I don't know," he said.

"Are you glad that I came? Everything was boring, wasn't it?"

"What's happening at the hospital?" he asked.

TxuTxu sat around the blazing dung fire with the Chief, the War Chief, the TiTi Chief, and the Chief's three sons.

"When must we kill them?" asked the middle son. His father raised his hand for silence.

"You have spoken wisely but quickly, TxuTxu. You have reminded us of our responsibility to Cee, to our ancestors, and to our medicine. But tell me, how will we enforce the vegetarian laws if we kill this Billy? Only this Billy knows the new Sanitary Vegetarian Code."

All the while, the eldest son of the Chief had kept his mouth silent. Finally it was too much. Tears broke the glaze of his eyes and streamed down his onyx cheeks. He rose and left the campfire before the others. It was the girl: Lois. She was never to be his quihairyp, his lover. They would put her to death first. She was the woman: the white woman.

Why go on? He lay down in the lippi grass and wept and then stopped weeping and prayed to his God. He asked for a vision, and then, the lippi grass moving in hypnotic circles around his body, the animal tufts breezing in scowls and joints of night soft in tiny wet pools, he came right up into the exploding watchtower of vision.

The plains of the land beyond the green fur, the plains beyond the tribal boundaries, were all tan and then gray and then open: flocks ran like bullets in a swarm through the yellow wind. Then a signal—a spurt of gas pierced the sky from the tip of a single wild tree; it speared five hundred yards into the air. He was alone. Walking on bare feet in the clay. Holding the ritual claw at his side and the twelve-foot lance. And then the animals froze. Their legs changed into circles, solid black tubes. Their eyes sucked back into their guts. Light beamed out of their tin heads. They no longer roared nor barked nor howled at the carrion moon. They ran as if on rails, bounced clumsily over stones, and tipped into ditches. The animals ignored his spear, for their skin was tighter and shinier than its point. They made the noise of geese.

He came to on the back of his tongue.

He wanted Lois the White Nurse.

How could he measure the value of that one desire? How to sort out the moments and classify them. He wondered if there was an Iron Law of Time: some moments must always be ecstasy and others must always be the clap. If so, how to find the ecstasy moments?

Gordon was about fifty and the leader of the Detroit Epileptic Movement. He was a big man, his fists were chunks. He had a moustache and he spit hot flame through his cold gray eyes. Gordon was sitting at the head of the council table in Debby Brown's basement, the headquarters for the Epileptic guerrilla group. He had an unpleasant job tonight.

"Debby, fetch me another Coke, okay hon?" called Georgie, the Epileptics' number-two man, their fine tactician. He also was a big man.

"George, what happened with them cinders?" asked Gordon, leaning over.

"Them? Me and Jackie ditched them two nights ago in the lot by Walker's Stationery."

"How is Jackie?"

"Well, Boss, to tell the truth, I just don't know."

Daisy ran up to Claudine and threw her arms around her. The two of them laughed. Daisy sat down next to the pool while Claudine went into the den to get another bottle of vodka. Daisy pronounced vodka "wodka" even though she was from Southern California. She had heard some smart Jew from New York do it that way.

"You full of shit as a Christmas turkey, George!"

"Hey, what's going down here, Gordon?"

"I'm talking about them cinders and about Jackie boy. You and Jackie forgot to cover your trail on them guns, too. I mean the shipment of pistols for this July. Cause they got Jackie this afternoon and your ass is hot as hell baby because I'm after you too!"

"Gordon, you must be making some kind of awful mistake here," said George, and then he laughed. Laughed and laughed because he sounded just like some rat in a movie he once saw.

"Just a little bit for me," said Daisy. Claudine poured two fingers' worth. Then she turned and smiled.

Vicarion looked over the fresh vinyl and clean turf of America, he saw the . . . distant mountains.

The drums beat out an invention in riot control. Billy

had been one of the soldiers dressed for months as a member of the Helping Hand of Jesus. The rioters were all just out of seminary. Their individual test scores had risen thirty points while they worked for the circus out of the charity of the Helping Hand of Vegetarians. It was going well. Thanks. Into the new enemy zone. The Woodstock Cigarettes made him freeze a vague bluish aroma like the beautiful rolling Lois spread-eagled on the golden ears of corn and thought of the movie code now under fire.

This pleasure is mine.

We going down on them mothers! he thought as he leaned in the shadow of the Afro House, a paperback book store where you could also get good soul food. He had his piece hidden in one of the empty cartons. Just then young Betty walked by and he saw her again as she had been that night dancing on Billy's chest just before that middle-class motherfucker left to take up his basketball scholarship at State. He was going to cut that honky's head. Next time he caught sight of that boy. He heard Billy was in Africa with the Helping Hand of Jesus, that racist prick! In any case, he needed a taste and another look at Betty's ass as she strode high and tight up the aisle of the cold-cut section.

In any case, Billy finally had an excuse. This time his visit to the hospital was legitimate and not just an opportunity to moon over Lois as she ran about filling prescriptions and putting hot compresses on the wounded boys, giving advice to the pregnant natives and antibiotics to the herdsmen from Yeelie Province. He swept the mosquito netting aside and there was Lois in her bra and panties.

"Excuse me." He turned to leave.

"Billy, here's your highball. Come in . . ." she whispered. He turned back to face her. In her hand was a tall glass filled with ice and dry London gin.

"How did you know?"

"It was no secret. All these months . . . in this jungle, O Billy!" she moaned, stepping out of her panties so he could see the inky hairs running in a triangle down under the nub of her body.

Billy opened his eyes. Lois was asleep on his shoulder. They were outside the tent in tall lippi grass. Billy reached out and pulled a handful of the bluish weed from the ground. Deftly, he shredded the vegetation until he had enough to fill a battered old pipe he always wore in his shirt pocket. He produced a butane lighter and lit up. The first draw was agony. The second went down like sand on fire. Then the third was . . . by that time penis with her silverpang out and resting up on the water shelf with iced tongs sinking in delicate swirls or red, red sonic viewfinders bashing his flashcube into the bulbous head. Softly, big as an orange, Lois took her bra and flash floods. He reached for the delicate lagoon. There for a soda the little pupils parading whining jet ultras for she sticks her elegant manicure up his penis. Silk panties stretched over thick come in her throat, her face an orange tent burning in the Arabian kitchen of icicle hooks bent into the aluminum gown. He signed the bill and gave each sponsor a pen. It took eleven hundred pens.

He was coming down. The consciousness walked across the jungle saying, "A pearl, a beginning!" We will eventually become "one" in some twelve-year-old's love poems.

They eventually got Nick Vicarion on the fourth day. He was on the floor of a Chinese laundry underneath a giant pile of towels. The three plainclothesmen were enraged.

"Go limp you cocksucker and I'll kill you!" shouted the sergeant who had a Teflon truncheon and a belt full of anxiety darts. He grabbed Nick's hair and yanked. Nick screamed but was quickly silenced when another shoved the butt of his Tommy gun into the bridge of his nose. Nick was screaming in his mind, I'm a father I'm a father today no I mean I'm a father how can they do this to me I mean I father daddy help your daddy me help father help me I mean . . .

They dragged him out to the car and one got in the driver's seat while the two younger ones jumped into the back with Nick. As soon as they were off, one cop grabbed a green anxiety dart and stabbed it deep into Nick's breast. He took another dart and scratched a bloody line up his face. The paranoia and nameless boxcars hit the ghost in isolation lungs he screamed Nick screamed like he had an underwater underwear net choking him into another hurt he was uptight tighter than the newest metal.

The roof was very dark and cool. Juanita stepped quickly from the light in the doorway to where Carlos stood. He was staring down into the street. He took her hand and squeezed it as she came to his side. It was August in East Harlem.

"¿Como está?" he whispered. She smiled slightly and kissed him on the lips leaving a trace of cool moisture there like a drop of sun condensed into pretty sweet water on the rocks of Vermont.

"I love you, Carlos."

"Quieres tu también, para siempre, Juanita."

Electron Eve was the fourth Tuesday in August. On this night, the nation gathered before their screens and sat mesmerized for four and a half hours as Mr. President threw barrage after barrage of changes into their living rooms. He sat in his blue suit and bulletproof Mr. President mask while the nation's children grew uneasy, whining and bickering until their parents had to tranquilize them and send them to bed. His speech was called the State of the States Address. Much of it was devoted to changing people's addresses: "Mr. and Mrs. Marlon Kandrac will move from 18 Pleasant Way, Nombe, Utah, to West Twenty-first Street, Newark, New Jersey. . . . Mr. Joe Gross goes from the second floor to room 2301 in his building. . . . The new address of the Rolf family of Dubuque will be 7815 Glenn Plaid Avenue, Inglenook, California . . ." The third hour of the address was devoted to world addresses while the last half-hour was time for universal truths. The adults of America hung on until time for the Eleven O'Clock News. Then a cloud of depression would settle like heavy fallout over the streets and the cornways; the police with their dogs would be set on critical alert. After a light snack, a little sleep, there were few incidents.

Up five hundred feet, the clean winds could go free, but below they had to scramble through the alleys of the city. The city was furiously hot, fire boiling down under the streets in the sewers and the underground. The furnaces and ovens, stacked one on another, rose up in a thermal upside-down cake, an asbestos glove to slap down your orange juice. Peppery specks clashed in millions of pink honeycombed lungs. In November, 1963, over 400 New Yorkers fell down with "speck attack" raging in their chests.

Billy was relieved when Lois took his penis in her hand and told him that it was the biggest she had ever imagined. Lois wanted to kiss him there but he was too nervous and instead they skipped through the preynini bushes to the oasis where they could bathe in pineapple oil and sweet Vermont water. "What I wouldn't give for a nice sauna now," yelped Lois, her head full of shampoo.

"You bet," said Billy. He was examining some mysterious tracks in the mud out back of the wash shack. They seemed a bit larger than the human foot and with splayed toelike limbs running in five or six directions.

Social science is like the science of human nature, at least that's the way Hobbes liked to think of it. He was the "father" of social science. Locke popularized Sensationalism. This was quite difficult for the older citizens of Europe to comprehend. It took Hartly to really explain it. But then Helvetius came along with his great faith in legislative reform and his belief that "self-interest" is always human nature. That was quite enough. Billy closed the book and went out to look for Lois at the hospital when the wire swung through his inner ear. He turned to see his attacker. Which direction first? Which attacker?

Man is the dirtiest animal. His pollution is driving him to look for an edge of the world which he can fall off. Yet he loves like no other animal. His beauty makes trees look like kings and his social science is able to explain almost any motivation. And his love and beauty, in a sense, are a pollution to the world. They spray emotion into green vegetation. Love is beautiful in the middle of the forest, and beside the bird sanctuary the gnarled hand scrawls out the right line. Every line is just there in Nature.

Billy was dried and in his clean, pressed, white suit. Lex, his "boy," came softly like a gerbil to the foot of his tent pavilion. "Lex, get me a bottle of that champagne. The pink kind." The boy was off in a spray of dust. Billy sat down and opened his diary.

Today I made it with the nurse, Lois. It was good and I thought it would never happen! She fell for the religious bit like a real sucker. Which, by the way, she is. She's from Rye, New York. One of those fools who thinks all Midwesterners eat nothing but Jello salad. Anyway, tonight I'm giving her the works: champagne, kneaded pâté of giraffe, lion steaks, mousse of lippi grass, and afterwards a dose of TxuTxu's "medicine." Perhaps I'll invite the Chief.

Lois arrived wearing her lemon-colored cocktail dress and rope sandals. Lex served them slowly, graciously, in the candlelight. Billy was a warm, engaging host. He treated her to countless anecdotes and toasted her beauty five or six times.

The Dean moved to his window and turned back one of the drapes so that he could look out over the south campus. Hall thought the back of his head looked like a shriveled-up and hairy gray buttock. That made him think of a cute ass he had seen in his eleven o'clock.

"Mr. Hall," the Dean spoke without turning from the window, with his left arm hooked behind his back in military pompous affectation, "you don't even understand what Time is, do you?"

"Minutes, hours, that sort of thing?"

"Mr. Hall, do you know what the rate of change is doing to the people of this earth? To the advanced people, the cutting edge of humanity? It's playing them at the wrong speed like Frank Sinatra coming through your head at 78 so he sounds like Donald Duck and the Chipmunks and all you can do is keep moving, moving. Where do you think you will move to after I expel you, Mr. Hall?"

Right to your bullshitting throat!

"Arhh, I thought I would get a job and then try and get a commission in the Coast Guard. That was Dad's outfit, sir."

"Bach will sit over here and across from him will be Mr. Handel. And then Mozart at this end, put Lorry next to Mozart, will you, Don."

Nikolaus sat patiently for all four hours of the meeting. He had heard these debates weekly for the last two years at Lettey University. The Left was always in trouble, the

Administration was always winning, it was always the same story. You couldn't get the neutrals to take the demonstrations seriously. The fraternity jocks wouldn't bother you until you had a demonstration and then they went berserk and clobbered you. So it was the same old story. Then Marsha came up and walked out of the hall beside him into the brisk Minnesota night. It was so dark with only the campus gaslights burning along Bicycle Path and Grayson Lake. Marsha was very short and bouncy. She was wearing no bra so her firm, high breasts tossed playfully under her thin blouse. Her hair was brown and soft and her face reminded him of a pixie.

"Let's take a walk, Nikolaus. How about it?" she said, and took his arm.

"Sure." And they started off toward the University Golf Course.

They walked for twenty minutes or so and talked little. Just pointed at a favorite landmark or glanced at the sparkling crisp sky of the new winter here in the great middle of America, the backbone.

It was completely natural the way suddenly Nikolaus bent down and kissed Marsha, first softly and then sliding his tongue into her sweet mouth which was wet for him and slightly sour and good. They stood there beside the Twelve Hole for about ten minutes, hugging harder and kissing deeper. Then, gently Marsha kneeled down in front of him and he went to kneel too but she motioned to him that he should stand and then she gently and innocently kissed him lightly on the penis through the rough fabric of his jeans. Then she pulled him down into her arms and they rolled over and over, rolled down onto the slight knoll at the edge of the smaller sand traps.

Marsha's panties were down around her calves in the wet grass and she was chilly as a globe of her pink ass slipped out from under the pleated skirt of Royal Stewart plaid she had bought in Atlanta two years before. Nikolaus was mouthing vagina, stroking his tongue in long sweeps up between the hot open lips and then driving it into the tight sphincter full of acrid juice. She was crying out very loud.

Then it was the other way around as she knelt over him and undid his zipper, then pulled, yanked his pants down and saw his large erection like a bright pole come into the starlight. She nipped at it with her lips. Then circled the head of it with a slow, wet tongue. Then went down and took one of his testicles into her wet mouth and sucked gently so that he felt his very sexuality grow confused tugging in many directions. Then she tried to swallow his prick. But instead sucked it up and down in long delicate flows of energy and sensation.

He turned her on her back and took his time easing into her slippery warm belly. Then he would rotate and swivel, drive, lunge and stroke until he suddenly stopped and she would keep going . . . whimpering and bucking and sucking his pole and then he would go again. He balled her. He made love like that for an hour and then finally he came deep into her. They were both full of exhaustion.

"That had absolutely no redeeming artistic value. I was simply fucking," said Nikolaus.

Later, his hands under his head and looking at the ceiling from his dark bed in the dorm, Nikolaus thought how odd it was that now he could have all the sex he wanted, the world was becoming more and more messy. The sexual revolution was a strange thing, he thought. Perhaps it wasn't a good revolution. But what the fuck is a good revolution? A good fuck, probably. Anyway, he had class at nine.

Billy was reading from his *History of Western Culture* while Lex prepared Lois for the ceremony. Her hands were tied behind and above her head, her bust thrown out and her ankles tightly bound. Lex cranks her up to the ceiling with Billy's winch attachment we take you now into the book: Jesus was the most crucial man insofar as he was of the species, more important perhaps than Adam for he was both the Gift of God . . . Billy put the book down and took a sip of his pink bubbly. "My God, Lois, you certainly look ravishing up there!"

She shook her head but was tightly gagged with a British flag-scarf. Billy finished his wine and swung his legs off the couch. He took up the whip gently, testing it slowly, teasingly running its scaly tip through his fingers. It was fifteen feet long and as red as fire. "This is going to hurt you, Lois. Let me assure you."

Was the beginning of the bomb
The end of the line?
Don't ask the linear men
And a bottle of rum.

"Gordon, this honky claims to be one of us." They were standing in the secret warehouse, the new headquarters of the Detroit Epileptic Movement.

"What is your name?"

"Billy, sir," he said. He was wearing a black silk jacket embroidered in gold, blue, and red with a glaring tiger and underneath the words "Khe Sanh."

"What's your last name, Billy?" Gordon was very calm and leisurely at the onset of an interrogation.

"Billy Fencer, sir."

"Where you get that jacket, Billy?"

"I got it in a poker game in West Lhoopville."

"The geese are running hot tonight."

"No soap, radio."

"Well, I guess you really are one of us. You know the new code riff and all that. With the Helping Hand, I presume?"

"That's it. I'm a courier right now. Got a message for you."

"What I want with a message? Me, I'm happy with no messages, like no message is the best message, that's my media, you dig?"

"From Thaddeus Mace," said Billy, standing just a little taller as he heard his own words bounce off the far walls of the flashlight warehouse.

"All right then, shoot," said Gordon. But one of his lieutenants, one Immanual, misunderstood and fired fifteen big slugs out of his scatter gun. The black souvenir jacket was suddenly a delta full of blood rivers. Billy was sobbing through his death pain. Gordon couldn't believe the dumb mistake and slapped his forehead, then pulled an orange dart off his belt and jabbed it into this Immanual's chest. A super nausea dart always fatal after two days of paralysis and seizure.

"Weep not for me, weep . . . weep for . . . America because . . . weep for her . . . because . . ." Billy was trying to remember the coded message. Gordon was on his knees, his ear pressed to dying lips. After a few seconds, the people in the cold warehouse saw a wave of vibrations pass down the thin body and then Gordon rose up.

"What was that he talk?" asked Debby.

"We're going to move Heaven and Earth. We are going to run across streets and play on three sides of every track. We are going to taste the emptiness that comes in the world's biggest ice cream cone. Right at the very bottom." Gordon finished his speech and walked quickly to his blown V-8.

Going

Rudy Kikel

Amused by the "psychology"
of our cinema, Lady France freed
    me from my frozen American
experience, my jock-shy gestures,

    said, laughing knowledgeably,
sex failure was not of the least
    importance, and led me on to
success, sending me, piggy wig,

    all the way home, on the one
trip I am always able to repeat:
    the closest thing to motion
in a past that seems cluttered

    with movements I was unable
to make: I didn't raise a digit
    (one for wee wee, two for ca)
when a substitute teacher took

    over our second-grade class,
remained pasted to my excremental
    seat, till I could stagger,
while Rosemary's father wondered

    at my pale face and strange
stumble, bandy-legged, way back
    to mama's analgesic hands;
the pause was always dying that

    preceded my step on a subway
poking into exhausted Brooklyn,
    dark head of my adolescence,
me hoping the doors might pop

open before my bowels surely
would; scared shitless or wildly
in love, I could not pull
a punch on the occasion of Fitz-

simmons' passing into certain
manhood, my books on the locker
room floor, my self-respect
a shambles, after I had scrawled

over his anally antiseptic
notebook, as others had scratched
it on mine, the oral dream
none of us knew we entertained.

Life is less fantastic now,
many of my secret wishes having
surfaced, but I still find
fingers gnawed, a page unturned

in books I am underlining
passages of, in not remembering,
not to have to become, still,
under Eros' furious and venereal

tutélage, periodically attend
adult education classes in toilet
training, apparently dead set
on remaining rather than on turn-

ing into, as a glimpse assures
one, of any complicated entrance
of mine or of my visiting fay
friend, the fabulous Morgan, back

into my safe apartment, glass
encrusted like a ballet studio,
wherein, likewise, externalized
eternal postures are assumptive;

uncertain now whether any new
options for actions will still
present themselves, nearing
thirty as I am, accommodated end

to end, in life as in love,
in three rooms that burrow back
        into the bottom of hovering
Beacon Hill, or whether whatever

        remains of the opportunity
for miraculous transformation now
        be only more possibilities
for the recognition of selves I

        crookedly became, but came to
becomingly because the *Schloss*
        was so exquisitely attended,
by refusing to lift hand or foot

        heartlessly, still, in either
circumstance, I have learned that
        the alternative to getting
hurt by going ahead is going dead.

Getting Out of Schools

Norman Martien

We are kept in school by parents and the law, and then by ourselves and what we have learned in school. Those who get out early, to get at life, are taught that they are failures. Those who stay in school, to be taught the arts of success, learn to fail at much of life. But both those who go and those who stay learn the games of summer vacation:

> *No more pencils,*
> *No more books.*
> *No more teachers'*
> *Dirty looks.*

Some find out early the real grimness of this rhyme, and when the law allows they attach themselves to summer's alternatives: a job, a car, a girl, an Army "career"—whatever advertises independence and success. It may really be success. But it is a reaction to schools, done with that defiance which masks disappointment, and when summer ends there remains a sense of having failed. The idea is kept alive by programs for failures, by names like "dropout," by employers who hire certificates rather than men, and by the memories of school orthodoxy. We all know men half-a-century old, competent men who know their work and their workmen, whose deepest shame appears in the drunken revelation that when they were young they quit school to take on life. Whatever tools and arts they master, they will carry to their graves a sense of failure, and their legacy to their children is the fear of all that schools do not call success. Their children will be among those who only play at summer vacation, who tickle themselves into a little life during the warm months of the year. The good taste of summer then becomes only something to get us through the winter. That same art of teasing, the living of a life deferred, may get us through to this and then that degree. And then it may sustain us through this job to the next, through this rank to the next—and finally perhaps through this life to the next. And finally, too, we may learn that the loss of life and time is the whole point of schools. Waste is what the schools are about. We are not just kept unnecessarily long in order to get what we want: we are taught in school to want to be kept. We do not just surrender much living to get where we want to be: we learn in school to want to be where we can surrender life.

In school we learn school, and there seems no end to it. Last summer, after twenty-five years in school, I sat in a tent in the woods in the Far West and considered that in the fall I would be returning to school. And then, as usual, I did go back, now to the other side of the teacher's desk and on the other side of thirty. I didn't stay in my tent in the woods, for I thought I had been in the woods long enough. I have been a very slow learner: I thought that I deserved many years of school because I was smart, and I did not think to ask how, at the same time, I could be simple enough to endure a quarter-century of what is called education. But I have at least learned from the foolishness of being in schools that school is not all I wish to learn. And I've learned from watching friends leave school that departure is difficult, that it may be only a desperate embrace of what we take to be failure, or a mere looking-glass exit into the same thing by another name. So I find myself now trying to learn how the vacation from schools can be taken more seriously—how we can vacate in earnest. That will require more than just quitting. A letter of resignation will do for a beginning, but I wish to be resigned to life and growth, not to failure. Freedom from school may mean freedom to learn, but only if we can also find a way out of other situations and institutions that are no longer fit for living people. While we make genuine departures from schools, we will also need to invent and discover paths away from most of the institutions of American life. Probably no one will be able to follow quite in the paths that I find and make, any more than I can follow those who have already taken their own ways. My maps would only get you lost in my paths. You'll want to get lost in your own. But I want to give an account of the ways in and out of schools, as well as I can see them now. Perhaps we can help each other to learn the times and ways in which such departures are made. Our wanderings will be a revolution, for we may come round to ourselves.

I GOT NOTHING, MA, TO LIVE UP TO

UNLESS WE KNOW EXACTLY what we're leaving, revolution may mean only turning to the same things by other names. Winning or losing depends on making out what is to be won or lost. So learn your lesson:

A. There is no such thing as an Institution of Learning. Learning is a living process, our institutions are lifeless abstractions.

B. The places we call schools are institutions where the power of the past dispossesses us of the present. This includes the power of abstraction, the power of ownership and inheritance, the power of destruction.

C. This grasp upon men and things goes under several false names: viz., Learning, Tradition, Service.

Schools are still the agents of our least lovely history. Our schools, as they have been justified, say, by Mr. Kerr, are still the kind of place that was projected by Francis Bacon. Whether we call them Multiversity or Salomon's House, their central functions have historically been those of reaching, grasping, and possessing. They continue to teach, in a poor literal way, that lesson of Genesis which says we are to "subdue" whatever life we encounter on earth. Even a school's small business is described by the possessive verbs and the vocabulary of acquisition: we get an education by taking courses from teachers (perhaps with tenure) who hold classes where we grasp subjects and take exams so we can get a degree. But this busy process is not *for* anything, except to gather the world into institutions.

In Bacon's ideal school, the "Father" of Salomon's House explains, "The end of our foundation is the knowledge of Causes, and secret motions of things; and the enlarging of the bounds of Human Empire, to the effecting of all things possible." Bacon's old scheme offers a revealing comment on our present schools, for he doesn't have to be embarrassed about consequences that have appeared since his time. Unlike our contemporary apologists for schools, he can afford to reveal the pointlessness of his knowledge factory. He can give us, with amazing innocence, his version of the mad curriculum of our megaschools. Among the activities of his College of the Six Days Works,

> The Preparations and Instruments are these. We have large and deep caves of several depths. . . .
> We have burials in several earths. . . .
> We have high towers. . . .
> We have great lakes both salt and fresh, whereof we have use for the fish and fowl. . . .
> We have also means to make divers plants rise by mixtures of earths without seeds. . . .
> We have also parks and inclosures of all sorts of beasts and birds, which we use not only for view or rareness, but likewise for dissections and trials; that thereby we may take light what may be wrought upon the body of man.

Bacon describes other means of collecting and subverting men and natural things, and since his time we have added some new subjects and fragmented some old ones. And we have extended this kind of process and its structures to corporate business and technological government. But in Bacon's ideal, and our actual, schools intellectual imperialism is the prevailing mode of thought. His college begins its functions with what is brought to it secretly from the world by "Merchants of Light." And still we imagine ourselves missionaries of humanism and benevolent technology, a source of light in a darkened land—but in our blindness we bring only fire and destruction to the world. One part of our schools, in research and study centers, devises "what may be wrought upon the body of man"; while another part of our schools, claiming to care for our being, provides and sanctions the forms and vocabulary that dress up our monstrous doings.

Like any abstraction preserved for a time, the American school has become a power of a few men's minds over many men's lives. A mere convenience of thought at first, it has become a Truth that makes all individual truths subject to it. In that respect it is again not different from other institutions. A judge in Milwaukee says, "We are a government of laws—not men." A university chancellor says, "A university is three things: an institution, a process, and people —in that order." An institution of learning or doing or governing makes allowances for you and I only so far as we can be abstracted and generalized. On behalf of efficient and ordered having and doing, regular boxes are made for all of us. In schools this is most readily apparent in a glance at the brick and glass box architecture. But that is only a hint. When we sit in a classroom we learn—so gradually that we don't know we're learning it—that there are also boxes for the mind, boxes for inner as well as outer selves. The classroom is a box within a box, and yet even within that there are boxes: department, curriculum, subject, course, syllabus, grade, credit, hour, degree. We are kept people, in a world designed for (and by) paranoia. What are we kept for? To design other and better boxes. What are we kept from? The world as it is and may be, things as they occur. Who are we kept by? The Biggies? The United Straights of America? No, we all cooperate in the building of our boxes. It is usually thought by those far within that there is someone at the outer edge of this Ptolemaic system of squares. But there are no exemptions and no outer edges, only different kinds of boxes.

The students live at the center of these old and angular constructions, and they get most of the pressure. They are by no means alone in their oppression, and it looks very comfortable and regular. So it seems just, when Huey Newton says that the white mother-country radical doesn't know real oppression, but only experiences it abstractly. The students guiltily agree. But in the ghetto as on the campus, abstract oppression is at the heart of our illness. The cops, the rats, the slumlords, the brutality are enemies that can at least be known, they can be seen and felt, found and opposed. But in the ghettos of institutional power there are only the nameless procedures, the faceless necessities, the smiling and shrugging at blank and arbitrary walls. Institutions make all people niggers. Every man shuffles and looks away from the knowledge that he is tied to corporate convenience by the gut strings of other men. Those who learn to live here only learn to fail at life. Your local school is a ghetto of the young, but the realization is kept from you by provisions of physical safety, by official terms and procedures, façades for the body and mind. So you probably learn less about living while suffering the same systematized poverty of life. Students who disrupt universities with violence and obscenity are only exploring the analogy of school and ghetto. It is not a random metaphor invented and enforced by "agitators." Where the university responds with sanctioned violence and official obscenity, we are only witnessing the abstract made physical and concrete.

YOU TELL ME IT'S THE INSTITUTION . . .

STUDENTS LEARN their school lessons well, they learn to act and believe in the structures around them. When they have had the satisfaction of saying, "We've made you show yourself as you really are," that is called a victory and they return to the known games of mental compartments—student committees of student government in student offices in student centers. Most have learned to have very little trust of themselves, and so instead they put great faith in the acquired content of their acts and ideas, new stuffing for the same old boxes. They are taught, partly by lecture, mostly by subtle forms of bullying, to abstract doing from being. I think that's why they bother to "take over" universities, why they don't perform the essential act of just walking away. They don't know how to walk away, just as I didn't know how. But if that is their ignorance, it is also simply good faith. They remain not out of laziness, not just because of the draft, or the ivy, but in fundamental trust of their teachers and teaching institutions. And in return their trust is betrayed. They are so wrongly taught that when they are most outraged and disaffected—what do they do?— they "take," place themselves within, the very center of their oppression, the very box of old boxes, the offices of presidents and chancellors. But really, who *wants* his office, who *wants* the buildings? "Give me two other guys and some food and I can hold any building on this campus for a week," a young man said to me. *Hold it?* For *what?* Let it go, let it go. It does not matter whether you are inside or outside a building, on this or that side of a wall, your revolution is lost when you have allowed old boundaries to define your position. Don't hold on to structures because old people value them. Don't join their committees to make recommendations to other committees to make proposals for reform. Use institutions, don't serve them. We say, "Well, it's bad here, but if it could be adjusted to accommodate our needs then we could stay." But that wish is not even right or wrong, it is unreal. If we can imagine such a thing happening, it would only mean that your needs have been institutionalized and you are serving the institution more abjectly than before. But it can't happen, for an institution is not just a framework within which your needs may be contained, like fruit in a jar. If you put fruit in a jar you have only jar preserves, not the fresh fruit itself. The container defines the content. It does no good to reform the jar, it is still only a jar. It does no good to put up new kinds of fruit, it is only canned fruit at last.

INSTITUTIONS cannot be reformed. What we call reform is a kind of small and expensive adjustment that an institution has to have just in order to function smoothly. Propose more than you want, accept less than you can live with—such is our practice, and so we use up our lives helping institutions to administrate our lives more efficiently. Names like "enriching dialogue," "constructive criticism," and "reasonable suggestion" only signify so much verbal grease for the mills that grind us down. We use the vocabulary of institutions, talk the language of walls, and so our criticism and dissent only nudge the existing boxes and place them in more comfortable arrangements. At best, and finally worst, we make new boxes. And, terribly, most of us *know* that's what we're doing, but we are taught in schools that so much shuffling is all we can reasonably expect. We learn to anticipate failure, to imagine a void of despair between perception and action, desire and statement, expression and response. We institutionalize these expectations, and so our gloomy irony is seldom disappointed. We learn to put on

a winking acquaintance with innocence and experience—
that myth of failure which justifies and explains all suc-
cessful lying and dishonesty. Ironic institutions confirm us
in this wise and gloating habit of thought, and the power
of seeming to know more than others gains us a power over
their lives. Like Southern governors, our masters and
teachers say, "These nigras can't do anything right; they're
just born that way"—while with the other side of their
mouths they dictate conditions and institutions that insure
the truth of what they say. And so we learn, until we cannot come to new life without a smirking irony, a skulking
dishonesty masquerading as wisdom. We read it in our
history, and suppose that all hopeful human ventures have
ended in periods. We hear it in the double-talk of corpora-
tion presidents and college deans. It can be seen in the
smiling chicanery of a political convention or a faculty meeting. And then we read it in the faces of the young poor, in
the papers of young students, and all have learned an aged
cynicism. The student will become an old reformer and
the poor will smile and vote for him.

UP AGAINST *WHAT* WALL?

WE LEARN in school to act like mere fallen creatures, able
to exercise freedom only in relation to someone else's limits,
derived from someone else's history. So we stand at a wall
and call for our freedom because we think it is someone
else's to give to us, because we think it really should be
kept from us. Thus we allow no respect to ourselves, but
only pay homage to walls. It is time we took our chance,
to try to live without boundaries of mortar and stone and
thick piles of dead language and old tools. We may learn
to dismantle our enduring monuments of junk, and as we do
this even the old junk may be put to new uses. While some
are learning the arts of departure from schools, they will
also be doing it. Better than talk, they can demonstrate how
it is done and take that knowledge with them to other
places. That is how our schools may best inform now, while
attention is still paid to them. That is how they might really
be showplaces of learning. They may be used as demonstration models—places where we can *show* how the struc-

tures of institutional life are dismantled, put away, and how the new spaces are used for living.

It is said that students are ineffectual revolutionaries, for they don't know what to do with buildings when they "have" them. That is their best hope. They play with switchboards, they nose through papers, they sit on desks and stand on chairs, they groove in the janitor's room and ball in the dean's office, they dress for a party and sleep on the floor, they bar the doors and jump out of windows. I think that most students (and some of their teachers) learn more from a few days of such serious play than in all the dreary years of business as usual. They are learning to leave school, they are making paths out of boxes. They are done with institutional walls, they are walking through them. That's why the play is both fun and serious. It isn't the rising of the masses, but neither is it just the house niggers' hoedown. Such play reminds us that each life may be a nova of many dimensions. When that is found out, a life around walls will be "mere" play, and it will be clear that the greater game is elsewhere. But learning this game will not be "mere" play either. It will mean more than closing the eyes and breathing deeply. It will require some hard lessons in new languages and new arts. And to find out new lives we will have to learn how to play with old tools of language and craft. We will have to play well, and not use our realities as if they were weapons or walls to fend off the world's changes. A child uses forms in that way, for he needs a few supports to keep the sky from dropping in on him while he explores the world. But our schools only keep us beginners all our lives. We can learn instead to kick out the props. Try it. The sky won't fall, we'll only arise. Our old metaphors hold nothing up, they just hold us down.

THE DEPARTURE FROM SCHOOLS and institutional structures will not be done by program and diagram. We may use such things, but that is a different matter—as the child makes plots and schemes only to try out the solidity of the world. Do research by all means, have programs if you wish, but use these like any tool, and discard them when they have served your ends. Do not make grand strategies for this and that betterment of the world. Your tactics are your strategy, for you must learn by what touches you and what you are in touch with. Don't worry that people say you are not far-sighted; they only mean that you have no designs for other people's lives. There is no need to save the world: it hasn't yet been discovered.

When schools are used to teach lessons about institutions, it need not be so tiresome and literal as most of our schooling. An inept teacher who has got hold of some piece of a truth will shove it at his students in the classroom; he will confront them with exams and grades to insure that they have accepted his lesson. Both he and his students will remain in possession of some brittle and useless fragment of knowledge. Mostly, he and they will have learned to distrust each other. So when students find a truth of their own, they shove it at their elders with signs and slogans, and when these seem to fail they confront them with the destruction and occupation of buildings. Their tools are more obvious, and so they seem crude, but their methods are learned from the very teachers who denounce them. Now there may be real use in a teacher's lectures, and in his asking his students what knowledge they have acquired. And there may be real use in students' distributing pamphlets and carrying signs, and in their demand for some responsive acknowledgment of what they have said. But the learning outside of the classroom has an advantage, for it can allow for that play of experience which teaches us our more memorable lessons. I don't think that the classroom will ever offer more than a pale shadow of this kind of learning. When we come out of the classroom to learn the ways out of our old schooling, we will want to find out how to use this advantage.

Because old reforming games have been abandoned, we have supposed too often that when signs and slogans fail of their effect, the next and only alternative is violent confrontation. For example, we may march in front of a building asserting this and demanding that, usually to no avail. And usually we have supposed that the next step is in response to the shout, "Let's take it," and so we sit inside, take all the play out of the situation, and insist that it's Them or Us. I don't say that these alternatives won't remain possible, but our tactics ought to have a little more wit than the politics of escalation. Instead of learning from inept administrators and arrogant politicians, we might learn how to create an educational drama of experience. Instead of imitating Mr. Hayakawa or Mr. Johnson, we might learn to become serious students of informing play—from people like John Cage, Ken Kesey, Abbie Hoffman. So instead of locking yourself into somebody else's building and somebody else's game, play with their structures, use their old props and scenery to teach a new truth. Instead of "taking" a building, say you've leased it to the administration in return for their allowing you to live, have a formal ceremony for the signing of a contract, have a grand reopening, cut a red ribbon in front of the main door. Or leave the building to its original owners, announce that they are to be held captive there every day from nine to five, post a guard of mock police, grant special escorts to the president when he goes to lunch, ask for ransom money from the corporations that use your school, hold a public ceremony for the buying of certain administrators and teachers, using Monopoly money.

This only sketches some possibilities. Some of the games may use more dangerous props. The most useful tactics have to arise from the point of particular circumstances and change from day to day, as new situations arise from playing with old kinds of living. Whatever overturns or rearranges an arbitrary and unjust order of things, whatever exposes the harsh facts underlying our educational fictions, whatever seriously questions corrupt business as usual—these are the activities that will create real learning situations in schools. People who perform such play will be called troublemakers, or childish, or worse, and some will suppose that this is no more than old agitating and muckraking. There is no doubt that such play will be considered dangerous, and dangerous people with power will come down hard on your revolutionary fooling. There may be no way to avoid this, only ways to know what to do when it happens. The difficult trick will be to keep such situations playful, to keep the rules responsive to the moment, even ahead of the moment —so that those who make and extend old rules will seem to be taking a part in your new play. Perhaps the power of your games will teach them the experience of play. Perhaps they will meet you as men and women, rather than as servants of institutional games. The people in school might, for a change, learn something.

SUCH GAMES will always be scary at first, awkward and confusing, but after a while random collisions may become random encounters, nebulous curiosity may become patterns of questioning, wondering may become learning. Of course I don't know how this would happen, I can give no guarantees, none of the timetables and borders and documents that are now supposed to assure educational products. As old games are discarded people will see that new kinds of play are needed, and so new games will be invented. New ideas of order will appear. We might learn, for instance, that the schoolyard wall is an arbitrary boundary, that on either side there is much the same proportion of wisdom and foolishness. We might learn, too, that some people, in and out of schools, are very good at the things they enjoy doing, and that this has little relation to accidents of title or of performance within certain structures. The difference between them and others will no longer be defined by the names and categories of institutional schooling: student/teacher, permanent/transient, old/young, professional/amateur. There might be, instead, a difference only between those who come to learn and those who learn in such a creative way that their curiosity and inquiry has the power of informing others. Their learning is an experience shared with those who learn. Each of these curious inquirers is a department of unlimited courses. He is his own credentials for what he does. He will say: I am a university. You come on over when it looks like we may share a commitment, and we will read or talk or work together. We are a university. There are no limits to what we may ask of the world. Perhaps there will be limits to what we find there, but we will be free to find them. If we discover that certain contours of our thought resemble old disciplines, then we will have found for ourselves a new value in them and an old dependency in ourselves. If we find that some stumblings of our minds resemble old limits, then we will have gained a new humility. And if we learn to play at cosmic wit, and find new landscapes in a strange world, well then we may also be humble in the memory of our old and habitual clumsiness, we may recall with some embarrassment the schools of wood and stone and concrete boxes.

LAST SUMMER, during my vacation from school, I lived in a tent in a wood on a cliff above the Pacific. The tent seemed very flimsy, for the sea pounds and shakes the shore, boulders and trees fall in, the water crashes and foams up fifty feet in the air. It was very wet there, almost like living in the sea itself. I awoke one morning to see the shadow of a crab sidling and clicking over the roof of the tent. My son Philip thought it was a spider, and at first so did I. But there are no spiders in the sea, I told him. Sometimes, to dry out, I would go out for a walk by the sea. It's not so wet there as in the tent. Even the walls of a tent may hold in more than they keep out.

Once I went for a walk in the late afternoon, about six o'clock. At first I walked through woods along the cliffs, then down a canyon and across a small stream. From there I followed a path that led out to a point at the land's end. The sun had come out from the fog about an hour before, but I didn't feel it until I had walked almost to the end of the point. There the woods stopped and the path went on through dry grass and scrub brush. Then, almost at the end, the path forked three ways. I followed it straight on and it ended at a sheer cliff. I returned and followed the left fork and it also dropped off straight into the sea. So I went the third way. The path went down steeply with high brush on either side. After about a hundred yards the path ended at the shore. I guess I must have been about two hundred yards from the far western end of the land. Maybe it was more, I wasn't sure.

The shore was littered with large pieces of rock, broken boulders, hunks of driftwood, seaweed all tangled among little bits of shell and brownish foam. It was difficult to walk on the broken rocks but I went slowly along the edge of the point out toward its end. I made my way around a large rock that thrust out from the base of the cliff, and I went on out of sight of the path.

It was strange and lonesome there, walking out to the far western end of the western shore. I went slowly, walking toward the sun above the sea, among the wreckage of stone and wood and shell. The tide was coming in, foaming and rushing in upon the shore's confusion. Small pieces of wood were beginning to float loose from where they had been stranded. Small round stones clattered among the larger rocks. The land seemed to be getting loose, indistinct from the sea. Then as I looked ahead I saw that there was a deep cleft in the rocky side of the point, and beyond that the cliff turned and there was a wall of solid rock out into the sea. It crossed the litter of the shore and reached out into deep water. I would not be able to walk to the end of the point. I guess I didn't much care.

But I didn't turn around right away. I walked on, more slowly, stepping from one rock to another, walking among them, stopping to look at pieces of driftwood. It was warm and comfortable now. Then I saw on the shore a small round rock, about hand size, smooth, but broken in two. Among all those broken pieces I saw these halves of the same rock. I leaned down and picked them up and holding one in each hand fitted them together. They made one rock that you could hold in one hand. By holding it tight you might almost make the break disappear.

And I thought as I held the rock, it's almost together, and if I throw it like this into the sea maybe it will be a single and solid rock again by some magic that I may not know I possess. But then I held it too long, for as I turned it I saw that there was yet a third piece broken off it; and before I could turn to throw it, there was the litter of broken rock everywhere around. Perhaps that piece is here somewhere, and perhaps it, too—but then each fragment and shard everywhere must join somewhere to the pieces I held in my hand. I threw the rock gently and its pieces splashed and disappeared into the incoming tide. I walked a little farther out on the point to look into that cleft in the rocks, but then behind me my son Philip called out and he showed me a pretty rock he had found. So instead we went to look into the sea life of the shallow pools left by the morning tide.

HANGING LOOSE
AND HANGING TOGETHER

SCHOOL MIGHT BE ONLY a name for learning to find and invent the skills and tools of becoming, not a place in which men are made and certified tools. Nothing is or means anything but what it is, everything is becoming, nothing can be held on to. All tools may be used, whatever we can find or invent, but we should not grasp them too fiercely and then live for them. Ways of thought are just various and beautiful tools of becoming, but we think so much of them, and we mistake them for what we are. A school that would help people to learn the wisest use of the tools of language and art and craft would have for its principles only movement and change. That is its foundation, theory, and practice. We could call it a metaschool.

In the sense that we now use the word, I am saying that we shall have no school at all. Because in a metaschool we will learn in the way life teaches. So it is also a lifeschool. I know that lifelearning is often rough and slipshod, and that it usually teaches people only to be frightened of change. But look at the kind of lifeschool most people learn in: their teachers are only able to teach in a rough, slipshod, and fearful way, for it is all that they know. Their own teachers have taught it to them, and others to their teachers, endlessly, and the lesson is driven home by the economy of greed and the politics of hate and fear. In or out of buildings, most of us are graduates of that American lifeschool. It is an institution. Yet even with all this, people are tough enough to remain human and good, more so than we usually suppose in our occasional glances in and out the schoolroom window. Like other institutions, our schools of life or learning teach us to disguise our humanity, they teach us not to recognize it in others. It will be the business of metaschools to find that life, to go with it— not to "teach" it and then hope that our smart talk will soak down into other parts of the social sponge. In a metaschool we will live among our lessons.

But we are all going to ask, as we find our ways out of our old schooling: Where can I go? How can I live? How do I find people? How can I go on learning and teaching?

Where can I find tools? And still, How can I *live?* When we have really found ways out of institutional living, I think we will only say joyfully, How can we *not* live? But I know that on the way to this, there will be some hard practical questions. And only your hard practice will answer them for you. For the mere theory of it, the question of where you live has only the simplest answer: it doesn't matter. Go where you *can* live, go anywhere and everywhere, go where you are. Your metaschool may for a time be a city, where you work with the arts of the streets; or it may be on top of a mountain, an adventure in higher education. Our geography is endless. You will know your school when you arrive there.

In finding where we can live, we will also have to find means to grow and learn. The plain questions of food and shelter may bring some pinch to our new schooling. Those who are very fortunate will find work that will fill more than the stomach. Many will just waste part of their time, in the pointless work that's so easy to find, and then try to live with what is left over. Others will want to find people to cooperate in the getting of necessaries, taking turns at work, inventing jobs, creating simple industries. Whatever means you find, you will have begun to learn your needs and wants, and you will begin to see the needs and wants of others. With other people, no matter how closely or loosely, you will have begun to be a metaschool, part of a changing and living community of learners. Don't worry that you're not a crowd, or even a tribe, not carrying your message or style to the world. That's not the point. Staughton Lynd said that some time ago, and he has been in and out of schools enough to know: "The spirit of a community is not, 'We are together to accomplish this or that end,' but, 'We are together to face together whatever life brings.'"

PEOPLE WILL COME to your life and your school as you come to theirs. Don't go after people with the responsibility of the intellectual, for that assumes that the power of mind is a power *for* or a power *over.* Responsibility to see clearly and to speak of what you see does not belong exclusively to any group, but to all men with their many kinds and degrees of light. Don't assume the bright man's burden and insulate yourself from the world's changes. Just listen, then talk with people, perhaps learn to build something together, learn together where you are, ask what you'll want to do, wonder where you'll want to be. This is not a license for bullshit. You will have to *know* what you're talking about, for now in every way your life depends on it. Don't make yourself an "expert," simply be honest to your own life's needs and don't impose them on others. Learn to find and do what is needful among men and you'll accomplish more than a century of lectures and tracts. And best of all, you'll be alive.

A metaschool may be a place, or it may be the inclination of a number of people. Learners might find out other learners and they might sometimes get together to teach and help one another. And there might be a continual flux among metaschools as people move on to other questions and other teachers. Only for the very young children would we really require a place, a building. They are not to be shuffled around, nor are they to be "sent" to learn. Perhaps they might first come over—or down, or up, or out—to your local metaschool with a parent or older child who wishes to exchange questions and views. Eventually, like the rest, the child would pursue his interests on his own, following out some question that interests him. This process would not create narrow specialists, but would encourage what John Cage calls commitment:

. . . This point is it. That point is you. We draw an arrow between the two points, indicating that you have dedicated yourself to it, unquestioningly. That is commitment. Where does it get you? Well, there are lines from that point that is it that are arrows to every other point in space and time. Any "it" is like a Grand Central Station, or rather a space platform in orbit. Once there, you can move out in any direction.

Grand Central Station—or a space platform. That is a small choice if you have already chosen to pursue a question about your life, if you are a full-time student in a metaschool. Of course it may mean a large difference in the number of other people you encounter. One may be alone in a crowded station, but on a space platform you will surely notice it. You may find that your metaschool sometimes has an enrollment of one, and gives a degree in lonesomeness.

Being clearly apart and alone may be useful. Crowds of people and things entrap our minds and make us think the world and we are grand and permanent and unchangeable. I don't wish to abolish all gossip, garbage, and gimmicks. So long as we find use and life in such things, let them be. Play. But we need not, I think, cram ourselves exclusively with such stuff. We chatter to cover up what we do not have to say; we throw junk into our lives to fill its empty spaces; we make lovely tinsel arrangements to enlarge and insure our prospects. We all try to be president, to keep on top of all possibilities, and so we busily steer our clumsy iceberg lives through warm seas toward imaginary harbors. As if everyone didn't have some silence and emptiness and blindness.

A metaschool would have exercises in shutting up, midterms in letting be, finals in being still. If you're living in your life there is no need to endlessly patch and putty its edges. Let your self be. Practice letting things go until you find out what is or isn't you, learn where your living ends and where you begin to merely make your living. Trust what you do, let it be. If it is good then it need not fill volumes, it will fill the world instead. A metaschool will not pretend that we are all such a big happy multimillion bunch. If we are alone, we will honestly learn of our loneliness. Then we may find new ways in which we are together. We may learn to travel light in order to make easy the difference between company and solitude. We will learn to make strong and light the things that we wish to carry and exchange among other men. Perhaps we will find that most of our books might be made more cheaply, of something that would enrich our gardens when we threw them away. We may find a few worth carrying, so he that runs may read. A journal of needful things, something like *The Whole Earth Catalog* now offers, might let people know what books and tools and toys are around. And like their traveling store, educational warehouses might move around the country from one metaschool to another.

These are just notions, but I think that when we need to we will keep our media light and efficient and living. And perhaps, each in our metaschools, we will even learn what we all along wanted to say and give to one another.

ONE OF THE SIMPLE advantages of school is said to be in the number of young people present in one place, and in the many kinds of encounter this makes possible. I think that this has some truth to it but that the price we pay for it is far too high. An army, after all, brings together many people in many kinds of meeting, but as an educational model it has serious limits. In a metaschool we will want the advantages of such meetings and collisions without the disadvantages of keeping people in boxes. Partly this effect is provided now by free universities, free radio, and free presses. As these become willing to let go their "underground" status, as they insist on being more than just "counter" this or that stupidity, they will help us to bring our schooling together. The "little" newspapers, because they are more consistently available than daily radio, and more flexible than a "free" curriculum, will probably be of most use here. Their major drawback is the provincial limits of their reporting. Although this is offset by an organization like Liberation News Service, it might be useful to create a mailing house for all such papers. This would require some funds for stamps and such, but it would be worth a lot to make it possible for every paper to send a number of copies to the mailing house, and to receive in return every other such paper in the country. Every newspaper office might be a reading room where we could learn of events and situations and people who don't get into the respectable papers and magazines. We would have in effect a national free press, news from the people who live in it.

But there are many learning situations that will not fit into the forms of either "courses" or "news." For these we will require a catalog of schooling outside of schools, a directory of metaschools. For every place where many kinds of learning encounter are possible, we might have a Learning Book. It would appear, say, at midsummer and midwinter, and it would list all the people, occasions, resources, situations, and places from which something might be learned outside of institutional games. It would include courses with teachers, where a subject admitted of that kind of learning. It would include apprenticeship situations where one might learn an art or craft of some value. It would include the kinds of jobs now listed in *Vocations for Social Change,* where one might work with some profit to more than his purse. It would include the places where materials and books might be made available. It would list places like zoos and museums and old buildings and tell how they can be used for learning. It would include situations, when they are known in advance, like conventions, circuses, rock concerts, demonstrations. It would include the locations where one may gather such news, where others may be found to make new kinds of situations: community houses, homes for runaways, political-action centers, friendly places. One of these places might be a metaschoolhouse, perhaps no more than a room with a phone. Like the newspaper offices, it would have a Learning Book from every place in the country, and then for places outside the country. So instead of a world university, with a world of trouble, we might instead create a World Learning Book. There is everywhere to go with such a project, so long as we remember that the Learning Books are only an index to the world's changes. It would take us a while to learn how to use this index freely. But in finding out new ways for learning, and in putting them together, we will be living with new arts in a new school.*

* A first version of such a book has been put together, for St. Louis. It's called *Livings: A Guide to the Other St. Louis.* Many of us contributed research and writing, but most of the work was done by Marc Feldman, Carole Remick, and Alan Stein. Most of the funding and the workers came, in various ways, out of a university, which shows how readily schools may be used to replace schools. The book is something between *Fuck the System, Vocations for Social Change,* and a college catalog. It is put together in nine sections: Education, Services, Organizing, Peace and the Draft, Media, Cooperatives and Communes, Places to Go, Ecology, and Resources Wanted or Offered. The divisions aren't altogether satisfactory; we find that we've overlooked many things, and many desirable things were just not to be found. But we surprised ourselves when we found that there was enough to fill seventy pages in a city where the habitual complaint is that no "other" community exists. The point of the book will be in how it is used, but as of this writing

All of this is only a sketch of some facts and possibilities. They are mixed with many fears and hopes. Institutions are not going to cooperate in their disassembly, nor can we even expect the freedom of movement that will allow us to ignore them. This summer I'll leave school, for a long, long vacation. Yet I wonder if I'm not beginning ten years too late, if the times will allow us room enough to play between advancing armies, while we learn the arts of life rather than death. We must learn to play true guerrilla games, walking through walls, using arms that reach rather than arms that kill. It sounds hard to play and fight at the same time, but among lifeless institutions all human play is sabotage, all true games are revolution. We can only, as always, do as much good as we can, be as alive and intelligent as we know how, forbear, and fight when we must. The timing is all, but again I have no timetable, no strategy. Such things are for armies. If it comes to that, no doubt we will find timetables and strategies at need; but if it comes to that, I don't know that it will matter who wins. There will be no clarities for a good while, no answers except in the opening of new questions. Whatever schemes and dreams are perpetrated among our institutions will not look like a movement, except to paranoids. Some will cry that the mortar in the walls is beginning to loosen, that there is much falling of stone, that anarchy, chaos, and old night have come again. You will hear that from the watchers and warders of stone. But those whose care is for living men and women will see that the world is only learning to dance, that all things once again move and change endlessly. Then every wall will have become a constellation of doors. And every door will open into life.

---

we haven't had time to see how it will work. It's still a very small beginning, but we have found that the world "out here" is richer than we had supposed.

Letter to His Brother

A. J. Litwinko

You would not like it here,
a country man in the city,
air-conditioned jazz,

the news of death
and irresponsibility slipped
under the door every evening.

When it's hot like today
everyone carries a slum on their hands,
maybe an abandoned car.

It's too mechanical, too brutal
for you and your wife, your plot
of squash, your white husky

and your mustang
near the barn. Be glad
you're hundreds of miles

away from me and the questions
that grow from my lips
like a beard: how is it

with you all? Is your old house
still big and cool
in the long flat Ohio evenings?

Does the river still run by
behind the garden when you both
sit in the dark and fondle

your frosted gin and tonics?
Is your car still expensive and running?
Is your mother still alive?

The Dark Ajar

John Morgan

NIGHTS YOU LIE exhausted, reading yourself again.
All that finished business, those friends in Seattle,
locked churches—what good are they to you? In
Wheeling, West Virginia, the women you never had—
and you once lived for them. Slowly the raveling
jet stream knocks and enters, knocks and . . . how
sensitive the centers of your eyes, and how cruel.
You haven't a dream left. Come, friend, open the
chapel door. Here is your plastic shrine, the translucent, kidney-shaped abstract of the God. Give
your will to it and it will glow.

The Season of the Single Women

Paul West

Beachboy they call him, behind his back, to his face: bitch-boy, biche-boy, bush-boy, bshba, baba. Either way Nelson Churchill answers, which means he fits the label, lets the label fit, and he responds, at least shows the word can activate him. And all through the season of the single women, August–October, he does what a beachboy is supposed to do: no more, no less, not even when the excitements of the season fetch his Carib appetites up high, and not even when boredom on top of fatigue makes him want to go sulk in his shack half a mile inland from the suave commotion of the beach and the Hotel Cobalt.

Out of season he fiercely sows the field of his mind, each year rereading with decreasing difficulty his hardcover English translation of *Mein Kampf* filched from the lending library in Kingston, as well as *The Thoughts of Chairman Mao,* a flimsy paperback found in a deck chair near the open-air bar of the hotel. Studying Hitler, the loser, he seeks weaknesses to run down in Mao, whom he thinks a prospective winner. A third book, equally favorite, is Benjamin Franklin's *Poor Richard's Almanac,* a gift from Mrs. Cowdenbeath, the most generous (and most discerning) of the single women with whom he deals. She smiles when he quotes "God helps them that help themselves," and tells him to practice self-help whenever he can, which he does, not valuing what he gives and giving only because he's a beachboy biding his time before the bloodbath fills.

Beachboyishly grinning, he's forever thinking about the first of the mass executions he'll stage right there on the pink-white sands of the Hotel Cobalt's beach, the shallow mass grave scooped out with a bulldozer stolen from the bauxite mill a few miles away, the loudspeakers pounding

119

the doomed with his own specially written Execution Calypso, and his aides in white-and-gold uniforms swigging rum punch from silver yacht club tankards while casually firing their carbines from the hip with the other hand. Of social reforms he hasn't thought, his main passion being to clear the land, empty the hotels and the villas, assemble a sufficient corps of blacks to justify his title of Admiral (he by now having enough oral Spanish to mark the look-at, marvel-at element in the word itself: *mira!* Admira!-l). His mother was never quite sure who his father was, and such too he would make the nominal fate of the white—mainly American or Canadian—sun-hunters, of the white owners and residents, even of the eminent black novelist retired back to his native land from the fogs of London after receiving an OBE from the queen. He would like them all, just before the bullets mangle them, to arrive at anonymity through fright. And if he forgets anybody on his own version of the Day of the Long Knives, they'll pay for it by being hanged, drawn, and quartered when he remembers. That's traditional, he tells himself (whoever he is), their hearts plucked out and held aloft for the good ole Jamaican sun to tan.

ALL THE SAME, he is courteous. As he's now telling Mrs. Cowdenbeath from the sand where he squats like a retainer beside her aluminum chaise longue, he has studied at first hand the manners of whites during a summer session at the university college, during which he dismayed the phoneticians with an ad-libbed dialect he claimed was spoken by a fast-dwindling Rastafarian sect up in the northwest of the island. She says nothing, and on he goes. A two-man team sponsored by the college found no trace of such words, or even such sounds, in that region, and on its return reinterrogated Nelson Churchill, who by that time had revised his imaginary language into something quite different. The experts gave up on him because he wasn't serious, and failed him in his end-of-term examination. After that, he just happened to not report a fire in the phonetics laboratory during a faculty celebration for a visiting member of the island cabinet. Lamenting the local shortage of dynamite, he removed himself (having no encouragement to stay in the haunts of literate men), first to one of the lavish villas in the suburbs where Cuban whores had reinstalled themselves in business, and where he served as both a practice-machine and peacekeeper. Should he, he tells her, later on execute them all or have them become the property of the state? Not averse to waste, all the same he didn't fancy annihilation of the island's natural resources, whether imported or not. With this and other problems festering in the truculence of his mind, he transferred himself to the northern coast and there, like an ebony Job, sat in a wilderness to think out his future. Except that it was a wilderness of green ferns and enameled birds, with bananas a-plenty. Five days he stayed, unmissed (being jobless, familyless, without a friend to his name, and not yet wanted by single women) and primitively content, realizing he could stay there indefinitely, cooing to himself as big jets came in low over the forest in chunking blasts that didn't faze even the hummingbirds at their gyroscopic midair stations or shake the trees and the bananas more than the much-advertised offshore winds.

"A nice-sounding place," she murmurs, tilting her Universal Jungle Punch in its plastic coconut. "Alla that," Nelson uncouthly blurts, his mind wholly on his telling.

AND NOW, telling her the same story all over again during her second visit to the island, he has reached exactly that point, and she is all patience, having nothing else to do. Besides, now they are more intimate than they were, although still collusive strangers. Up, he resumes, was the blue of the bluing the fat black mammas dunked into their zinc washtubs to whiten what the sun couldn't bleach. Down, that was the ants, busy as soldiers, lizards that froze or ran, and olive-green moss. Everything else was trees and steaming heat against both of which he felt he could lean. All those bananas left a film on his teeth like soap only more sweet, and he always woke with a crick in his back, the ground, if anything, too soft; but he swanned his way through the identical days, and on one of them told himself he was finally born: not on the last day he later decided, but maybe the middle one when there were fewer jets than usual. And he stayed on to let his new self relish the site of its birth.

On his return to human habitation he cut his hair an imperfect short with a long strip of glass, bloodying his scalp in the act. Scavenging on the beach, he found two compatible boots encrusted with salt and algae, and then, with money earned by motor-mowing an entire sports arena, bought a pair of blue coveralls in order to offer himself as a mechanic at the resort's most run-down garage. But, laughed away because he looked like a giant sea urchin walking on two blue laundry bags, and the boots looked no more like boots than like kettles or conches, he ran halfway back up the hill in tears, mouthing improvised neo-Rastafarian oaths. An hour later, after having reviewed where he could and could not go according to taboos of skin and class, he made three resolutions, each depending on the others and on the season just started. He acquired a decent pair of beach shorts and a thin gold chain with a medallion, and began to parade himself on the beach near the Hotel Cobalt. He squired and sired as many single women as offered, learning from them some correct and fine-uttered English. And he read as many books as possible in order to found the Revolution when the time came and thus become the island's Land-Admiral. From that time onward he felt the sun making suction on the top of his head to make him grow taller, the sand plucking at his toes to make him stick around to be fawned on (just as he in turn fawned on the white-thighed, chuckling single women when he helped them out into the shallows), and the wind speeding him on to a gorgeous destiny.

"A good start," he recalls, lapsing almost at once into local brogue, "no' evin p'lice 'pon my trail. I wuz startin' clean."

Now, THIS BEING her third year at the Hotel Cobalt, he has told her his story for the third time; each year it has taken him longer to tell, not so much because he's had more to tell about but because he embroiders for his captive audience. Taletelling has become part of his duties, but to Mrs. Cowdenbeath only. Already an institution, he makes beach dates for the following year and accepts the gift-wrapped colognes, watches, gold-plated brushes, bird-of-paradise shirts and ties, with diplomatic gravity. Most of the stuff he sells off cheap in shantytowns in the beach's hinterland, all but the colognes, which he needs for the season, when, in the humid fug of his shack, he drenches his body with them after washing off the salt and his own musk in the rigged-up lean-to shower.

Told he's just too much, "nearly too hard to take," he smirks impersonally and tells whichever of the single women it is that his motto is "I Serve," which he has learned somewhere is the motto of a British regiment. Cavalry almost certainly, he thinks. The shack always amazes them, crude as it is on the outside and almost camouflaged with branches, some stuck into the ground, some tossed onto the roof. It has no windows but it does have a concrete door befitting a bunker, and this he's set into a solid log that turns between two wooden bearings that cup it at each end. The concrete he stole and poured himself, and the wooden parts he axed out in a day. A perfect fit, the door has to be lifted as well as pushed, which none of the women can do, and so—whatever he decides to do to them once they are inside—they can never escape him. But what amazes most is not so much his gleaming collection of stolen tools (saws, planes, chisels, mallets, and gouges), nor his library on ramshackle shelves made from crates and barrel staves (so some lines of books curve up, some down), and not even the walls solidly collaged from *Life* and *Time,* or the handmade triple bed with its quilt made from the flags of a dozen nations and the buff satin sheets that he actually bought in one of the gift shops; it is the iron trunk in which he keeps a reserve of pharmaceutical supplies in transparent plastic bags alongside jars of Vaseline as big as goldfish bowls and full of wan-looking lard. There are hot-water bottles, a couple of car aerials, several bottles of antiseptic, some lengths of ship's rope, a well-thumbed "blue" album which Nelson bought from an Egyptian mining expert in a Kingston brothel, and last, but noway least, a mint stack of towels. It is this that hones amazement into delight; each woman in her turn sees how worldly he is, how he'll succor her through every trial, every routine misadventure, and has even made provision against hemorrhage, which he'll blot both-handed like a Nubian bearing a snowdrift in his arms, all this between their swim together and her chilled vichyssoise alone at the Hotel Cobalt. Blood is on his mind, in many ways.

But Mrs. Cowdenbeath is accustomed to all of this; *doyenne* of his single women, she knows about the others and closes her mind against them.

"Good days," he tells her, "I'm free. Then there's the vexatious days when it's pay. And all the technique you got. *Where* you from again? Oh, yes." Widow of a light-plane manufacturer in Indiana, she used to go to the Virgin Islands until too many of her friends began showing up too; she smiles coldly when he says it. "All the best India you got. But mos' days I'm free, mam, and any token of your appreciation in the fullness of time . . ." He's learned from English tourists how not to end sentences, and then those vocal dots bulge and bloom in the other's mind and come home to him as dry goods minor and major inscribed NC, to be sold later by the light of paraffin lamps to sniggering villagers who regard him only in part as Land-Admiral and prefer to see him as a legal bandit: Nelzun de Screw, whose pistol is his pomaded pizzle. Or as a show-off ripe for plucking.

"Going cheap," he tells them on more than one occasion, all of his correct English having lapsed. "Silva back brushes. Brush both-two sides yuh hayd the same wun time."

They chatter at him, yellow teeth ocher in the amber light.

"Lokka, bristle to bristle," he says, and mates the brushes.

One of them motions him to make the brushes jig-a-jig, and he does that, as if making the brush-unit breathe in and out, leering his best and whispering the price thick-spittled into the faces next him. "On'y wunce ev' use', and dat to part de hayuz on a fine-fan ladee, as Gud-Abuv's my breadcart fulla witness." But no one buys on this occasion, although they start drunkenly brushing one another's hair, the men the women's, the women the men's, and suddenly one superabundantly buxom, fruit-gnawing girl called Drydock Nellie has one brush up her pinafore, working it to a rhythm that they all begin to chant and move to, the women symbolically palming themselves and yelping like scalded birds while the men guffaw and begin to strut, and Drydock Nellie now leaps with straggly flicks of her legs behind her, down into a crouch, then up with a hysterical shriek, both hands flying now and no sign of the brush on the ground. It lasts for an hour or so until several of them stumble away to sleep, and Nelson Churchill, his mind full of Nellie, bequeathes his brushes to the village (one of his communes-to-be, after all) and strolls away into the trees.

No skin offa my nose, he tells himself. I'm brush-happy.

NONE OF THE OTHER single women know he's the Land-Admiral-Elect of the Hotel Cobalt (his title grows in fits and starts); only Mrs. Cowdenbeath, who, as they do, calls him Nelson and who, as they are, is "mam" to him. "Services today, mam? Or do we just want to wade out and see the fishes? Cool off the lower parts of us." And some of them he picks up, *lifts*, with dexterous delicacy and bears to the water, as oblivious of black rivals (than all of whom he's a good two inches taller) as of white also-rans among the single women. This year he's booked over half his time —has, in fact, a clientele and, in some absolutely unfailing attic of his head, keeps a chart of each woman's appetite, background, and parting gifts. Mrs. Cowdenbeath, however, still comes tops: she wants to be, she's competitive and sensual. Each year, Nelson has provided her with about fifty paperback thrillers, which works out to be a couple a day, and services averaging nightly-thrice in his shack, to which he speeds her on his light motorcycle (as he does all the others, both the steadies and the irregulars). Bestriding the pillion, she has to keep reminding herself that she abolished jealousy, possessiveness—what *is* that goddamned emotion anyway?—many years ago when Cowdenbeath was stepping out on the spree that finally took him off. All Nelson knows, and cares, is that any woman who can read at that speed is entitled to whatever services she can afford. So he serves, and she counterserves with erotic tidbits gleaned from the anthropology and psychology shelves of the state university back home. Always, out of Mrs. Cowdenbeath, as it used to be said of Africa, something new—and sometimes what came out of Africa long ago. And always, too, as she departs for eleven months of planning, she gives him an ornate weapon as a gift, thus feeding his paramilitary obsessions. From his three years with her, he now has an Arabian dagger, curving and ruby-studded; a rapier like a sinuous shaft of steel light; and, most recent and his favorite, a ready-made garrote that has only to be screwed to the back of a high chair to be operational. Tempted, Nelson tested it on his own calf, winding the screw down and down, and then in and in, until he screamed sharp and sudden as he never meant to scream, and all he could think of was Adam's apples, how they must split them in the execution chair. Ggrruck.

No WONDER THAT on the night before she leaves the island, he at last tells Mrs. Cowdenbeath straight out (as distinct from minatory hints) how he, a Rastafarian, should regard the Emperor Haile Selassie, crowned Ras Tafari, as God and demand repatriation to Ethiopia. At first she thinks he said Rotarian, but just as fast identifies Ethiopia as Abyssinia. "Better tell you de trut, mam, us Rastas dun kid aroun'. Lokka mightee funny wid hair all in a bushy tangle; dat call' de dreadlock style. One day soon dey'll be runnin' all de island and de sufferation dat goes wid it an' none uv yuh cripple-up guvvernment folks. Rastas's offal sure of their saylves."

"Then," she begins, as he oils her shoulder blades preparatory to massage; but, prone, she can't see his face, the displaced-person glaze of his eyes. So she says nothing further. For several minutes the only sounds are the spondees of his breathing as he kneads the taut muscles of her upper back and her moans of pained relief.

Now he straightens up and says, rude: "You. Wheah yuh goin' tuh run tuh then? Where all the yuhs goin' tuh run tuh then? Yuh be tellin' me that?"

Before she can answer or even comprehend what was said, he's unhooked the concrete door and stalked outside into the soft, clicking night, his face all ashake, a voice in his skull repeating "Admiral, Admiral." Three years is long enough to wait. It's time. You wait an' longer you go marry Drydock Nellie kinda trash. Now is the . . .

Returning to the shack door, he nudges Mrs. Cowdenbeath to move back in, his muscles bulked in threat.

"You've nothing on," she softly rebukes him as she retreats. "You should—well, it doesn't really matter. No."

Ignoring that, he talks again about the Rastas, black heretics that they are, about Haile Selassie, Emperor of Ethiopia, the dreadlock style, the Land-Admiral-Elect of the Hotel Cobalt Bomb *By Appointment*—"like," he expostulates, "it sez on the liquor bottles and the jams and them boxes of fancy chocolates in the gift shops. By Appointment to the Royal Family!" And then, with accelerating fervor, he runs through the thrice-told story of his life again: the same three books he reads during the off-season, the nine months of enervating leisure, all of which she knows by heart. Again he tells her about the executions he will stage.

"You," she mocks. "And who else?"

Right back at her he blusters, "Yuh. I'm not no Land-Admiral for nuthin'. *I got men.*"

Instead of answering she stares at him hard in the semigloom, then hitches the big white towel right around her peeling shoulders as if all-of-a-sudden modest, and dips into her purse.

"Here." Ten twenty-dollar bills. She fans them out in front of his teeth.

"Whatta that fuh?"

"To tell you the truth, you're a big, you're a beautiful black boy. Caribbean gazelle Grade A. You're good. To me. You lift and fetch and carry and kiss my hand. All the rest of it too. You give me twenty years back, which is all the years you've had, and all I do is to deduct them from forty-eight, which is *all* the years *I've* had. If you aren't here next year I'll be upset. Put out. But I'll survive. And, I'll tell you something else. You've got no men. You've no more gotten yourself an army than I have wings. It's time you knew something, not everything, only this. You're no

Castro, you're a goddamned capitalist with a luxury dream. Take it—here. This is money, see? It's no use to me. Take it. *Nelson*."

He can't believe it, but say it she did. "To go to Ethiopia with, to be repatriated with." He guffaws, but an awful and far-from-air-traveling scenario fills his mind and enacts itself at speed. Chairman Mao reels backward, spitted through the neck on the Arabian dagger. Hitler paws at a feebly spurting puncture in his belly and the blue-steel shaft of the rapier strikes again, unheld, passing this time through his hand and onward. Sitting erect in a barber's chair, Benjamin Franklin himself adjusts the screw of the garrote tight against his Adam's apple and awaits the executioner's *coup de grâce,* the hand still at his throat as if cupping a broken collar together. Going, going, Nelson Churchill's brain squeaks, I'm in trouble.

"Read books," Mrs. Cowdenbeath is telling him. "*I* do. Find out things. Buy maps. Get out of yourself an—"

Nelson Churchill lets out with a strangled sound, far from guffaw, knowing no airline is going to refuse his money. To Ethiopia he can fly; boats go there as well.

"It's for services rendered," she tells him, hushing him. "Green and portable. Now let me dress." In dumbfounded pique he has taken the fan of bills. Benjamin Franklin is still sitting, braced heroically for the end, God not helping him because he's not helping himself.

"Abyssinia." She is giggling. "A word with an abyss in it. Ah'll be seein' yah! Seriously though, penthouse politician, that's you. Why, you'd be better off in Africa, at least if you ever decided to be an amateur politician instead of a serious capitalist, which's what you damn nearly are already. You, you're a shark, and I'm a bank. I'll die rich, you see. You'll just die. Now, you want more money? It's free. On the good days, like now."

The big images in his head go small, vanish, but his last sight of Benjamin Franklin is of a bespectacled black sage in arrested motion, hand still at throat, not helping himself at all. *To what?* asks Nelson. Mao the black cherub with jowled eyes is nowhere to be seen; Hitler of the wasting cheeks, black perhaps only with fury, dwindles to a point and also goes. Nelson motions at her gifts to him—the dagger, the rapier, the garrote—still dangling from their nails against the wall. She wafts them out of existence one at a time, hand left-right, then right-left, and up-down, like a traffic cop making room for a helicopter to land in. The money is green for go, she tells him.

"OK, beachboy, I'm set." Her mind commanding her eyes to distance him as soon as they reach the lights. She's like a moviemaker proving the outsiderness of an outsider by photographing him through a window.

A kiss on his brow in the beach's penumbra is all he gets, and that's too much. Angry in tears he races the motorcycle home to the shack and bundles his three favorite books together with as many of Mrs. Cowdenbeath's discarded thrillers as he can find into the towel she just wore. Soused with gasoline, they all burn fast, lighting up the small clearing he cut three years before.

After that, he isn't seen on the beach for a whole week; but, sometime during an evening, in the shack with his back to the door, he sits polishing the garrote with yet another towel from his supply and humming the first lines of his Execution Calypso:

> Mister Execution-Man, drilling holes in all them white-
> face animuls,
> Livens up de market-day—

At a touch on his shoulder he abstractedly says "OK, mam" without turning round, and that is all. Bushy-haired and bearded, the other Rastas spring into the gloom of the shack while one tightens the wire around Nelson's throat. They take the dagger, the rapier, and the garrote, as well as the dollars, but they leave behind the dumped contents of the iron trunk. Weeks later, two local constables in soiled white shorts haul open the concrete door and find the Land-Admiral of the Hotel Cobalt Bomb By Royal Appointment burned black on the charcoal of the triple bed, with not a single fly for company, so tight the fit of the door has been.

Veins

Robert Chatain

TAKING HER HAND I saw them all beginning
All leaving the eyes of her whorled fingers
Snarling up phalanges, metacarpals, carpals
Braiding radius and ulna, riding humerus
To the beautiful shoulder I admired
Also a mat of them blue and cool at her throat
Fed from filaments lacing her graceful features
Ropes climbed her other arm and spliced in
Tributaries emptied from breasts and back
The same was happening below but I didn't look

"Where is all this blood coming from?"

Like onions cooking her translucent skin faded
Like pine needles burning her bones softened
Soon she was wholly gone but the veins stayed
Gently I bundled them and lay down
On my back as their outline would not support me
The yielding familiar shape was almost my height
Holding them still I entered a narrow place
Where I sensed the tangle of veins redden

The Wharf

W. S. Merwin

From dates we can never count
our graves
cast off
our black boats our deep
hulls put out
without us

again and again we run
down onto the wharf named
for us
bringing both hands both eyes
our tongues our
breath
and the harbor is empty

but our gravestones are blowing
like clouds backward
through time to find us
they sail over us through us
back to lives that waited
for us

and we never knew

The Last Quixote

MARGINAL NOTES ON THE GOSPEL
ACCORDING TO SAMUEL BECKETT

Robert Coover

IT IS DIFFICULT to do this thing, to speak of Beckett. Indeed, he makes it difficult to speak at all. "To name, no, nothing is namable, to speak, nothing is speakable, what then, I don't know, I shouldn't have started." Nothing justifies the betrayal of silence, he tells us, so earnestly in fact we cannot hear the silence for the admonition; yet at the same time there is the compulsion to speak: "strange pain, strange sin . . . , you must go on, I can't go on, I'll go on." "The act," Beckett explains to Georges Duthuit in their "Three Dialogues" on painters (*Transition*, 1949), "is of him who, helpless, unable to act, acts, in the event paints, since he is obliged to paint." Why is he obliged to paint? "I don't know." A senseless endeavor and to no end, yet understandable. To be obsessed by mystery, by the impossible Self and the tyrant Other, by paradox and flux, "life and death all nothing, that kind of thing," is a malady, to be sure, but a malady of some ("human" is the word) dimension. But to be obsessed by and so to speak of, for example, Samuel Beckett? No, that seems merely pathetic. If not fraudulent. Adulterous.

How go on then? Well, it is sanity gives us license, call it sanity, call it a gift. Imagine, in the wise of exemplary microcosms (we are in a time, like Dante's, that tends to think that way again), not a circle, but just a center, without a circumference. Those who strike out for the edge are kept in Magdalen Mental Mercyseats, as are those who stay at home (the center is empty, of course, and they just fall through). The rest of us pass our lives, or something like them, fearfully encircling the voided core, minds averted, complaining of hemorrhoids, corruption, and climatical malice, clawing our eyes out (not in penance or in rage, but as a specific), indulging our appetite for motion, habit, and whoopee, lashing one another with our tethers. And what we trip over, we speak of, because why not? The fool and his banana peel—the artist, as they call it in the famous Mr.-B-and-Mr.-D routines, and his occasion. The incontinent artist. Any occasion. A corpse, for example, or a concept. A catalogue, a cunt, a Christian. Or some inscrutable ternary, some longed-for memory, some sweet disaster. Or even somebody, e.g., Samuel Beckett. (Between first writing this paragraph and revising it, I came on three different writers who, in speaking of Beckett, had recourse to the same image of parading around a dimensionless core. Beckett, after Pim, would smile at the congruity of course, "scraps of that ancient voice," a myth locked into us by language, "the remnants of a pensum one day got by heart and long forgotten. . . ." Yet, maybe more ancient than that even, yes, it may be a myth conferred upon us by our own nucleic acids, we can imagine anything if it comes to it.) Here then this ordeal, grope in a panic in the mud, speak of Beckett. "And me, about me . . ."

IT CHANCED that I entered upon my own novitiate about the same time, in 1957, that *Evergreen Review* entered upon theirs. Such occasions, whether for magazines or writers, are rife with audacities and manifestos, clumsy and contentious searchings for a new way with the dead words, a sifting through the silly clutter of one's earlier history for something of value and an eclectic embrace of all eccentric visions from abroad—for a while, for me, *Evergreen* was about the only game in town. And in their first issues, they published Beckett's "Dante and the Lobster," "Ten Poems from *Echo's Bones,*" and "From an Abandoned Work." This latter fragment, appropriately, was about a setting forth (". . . I was young then, feeling awful. . . . Feeling really awful, very violent"), a setting forth that was painful and ridiculous, mainly into the head and through words (". . . words have been my only loves, not many"), rich with pratfalls and paradox, and animated by a new kind of run-on phrasing, self-conscious, self-deprecating, self-contradictory, not unlike that of the stand-up comedian: "I was mad of course and still am, but harmless, I passed for harmless, that's a good one." He'd reached me, I was to leave no word unmet.

Others might have discovered Beckett even earlier, yes, of course they did, who am I to speak for others? After all, I bought a lot of dirty green books in Paris in the mid-fifties, but I didn't buy *Watt,* and they tell me it was there before I got there. Just as well, for I wouldn't have liked it, as I didn't much like it when, much later and an enthusiast, I read the Grove Press edition. And then, what about *Waiting for Godot,* and *Molloy,* and *Malone Dies,* they'd been out a long time, yes, face it, Beckett was famous, I was late as always, I who was at that same time discovering for the world the likes of Kafka and Henry Miller and Lorca and Sartre and Dylan Thomas. Dostoevski. William Shakespeare. I was very busy.

Such, anyway, was my first encounter with Beckett, and over the decade or so that has, in the hard world, transpired, I, like Bom (he must have heard something, nearly got my name right, Malone heard it: "And it doesn't matter to my head, in the state it is in, but the man carrying it says, Eh Bob easy!, out of respect perhaps, for he doesn't know me, he didn't know me, or for fear of hurting his fingers"), have crawled back to him from time to time, can opener at the ready . . . and did he know, flat out in the muck there, the poor saintly bastard, that, having heard him out, I got up after, took a bath, and went to the movies? If in fact there seems to be more of Beckett here than me, if quoting him seems to be my only way of getting on with it, it's because his epigrams have held up the walls of my studies all this time, one of *my* voices after all, no longer his, I say it as I hear it . . .

And I shall resemble the wretches famed in fable, crushed beneath the weight of their wish come true . . .

But not a word and on with the losing game, it's good for the health . . .

Yes, it's all easy when you know why, a mere matter of magic.

A trace, it wants to leave a trace, yes, like air leaves among the leaves, among the grass, among the sand, it's with that it would make a life . . .

That passed the time, I was time, I devoured the world. that's right, wordshit, bury me

At the end of the fifties, I was a student of sorts at the University of Chicago, and there was a lot of Beckett suddenly around just then, the whole trilogy, plus *Godot* and *Endgame,* reprints of the early novels, and *Evergreen* was publishing something or other every couple of issues. Even our own *Chicago Review,* being torn apart by the inane controversies that eventually set up, in protest, *Big Table,* managed to print a piece of *The Unnamable,* and a troupe of traveling actors brought *Endgame* to Mandel Hall. I remember that, after the play, I made some contemptuous remark about Beckett's weakness for hayseed humor ("the old folks at home"), and a really nasty argument ensued, no, I was not the first to discover Beckett. It might even be said he made it in spite of me.

Students are Beckett's natural audience, maybe the only one he's got. His is a secret text for initiates: rebellious, blasphemous, romantic (". . . let me down, shadow and babble, to an absence less vain than inexistence"), intransigently nihilistic, raucously scatological, a glimpse (from purgatory, where students live) into the living death of the bourgeois dreamworld, including the bourgeois novel, counsel and preparations. Though serious ("I was born grave as others syphilitic"), he turns his "wild beast of earnestness" loose on the grand "Where now? Who now? . . . Questions, hypotheses, call them that" of the student's dark passage, and makes them seem pretty funny, terrible maybe, too terrible for the silly Billy Graham world, but funny. He plays like a juggler with big words like *uniparous* and *mensuration* and *apnoea* and *emunction,* mixing them up joyfully with boghouse barbarisms, often pretending he doesn't know what he's doing. He lets a parrot reduce Locke's "Nothing in knowledge except by discernment" to a mere *"Nihil in intellectu,"* and warns the scholar: "No, don't pretend to seek, don't pretend to think, just be vigilant, the eyes staring behind the lids, the ears straining for a voice not from without, were it only to sound an instant, to tell another lie." He worries over improbable syllogisms, "clarifies" an object or idea right out of existence as a string of clauses undo each other in happy succession, makes the exercise of memory and logic seem like a game for idiots, and insists on more than a mind built like "an indefatigable apparatus for doing sums with the petty cash of current facts." He turns Sartre's *Néant* into comedy and, with what one writer calls his "frantic precision," shoots panic into the dry stuff of the logical positivists. As for pilgrimages and catechisms, the student's lot, well, if *How It Is* is too much of a drag, see Moran's brief encounter with the farmer at the end of *Molloy* ("Such sentiments could not fail to please a cattle breeder"). And for the dropout: "He began to talk. He was right. Who is not right? I left him."

Beckett offered us, me, I can only say me, offered me, in those days, a way of going on, of making art, without affirmation; he guided me when Christ and Tennessee Williams failed, served me as exemplar, wise man, and fool, kidded away my self-pity, and did what little he could to humble my brash posturings. He was wonderful at odd abrupt transitions between different fictional levels, at ironic echoes and parallels, funny games with numbers, names, and logogriphs. Of course, he also pandered to my own awkward fumblings with the inconsonance between words and their referents, making mere ineptitude seem meaningful (and maybe it was), pandered as well to my transient love of travels and trials ("in the toils of that obscure assize where to be is to be guilty"), to my aggressive inclination for obscurantism and academic gags, abstruse puns, rhetorical parody, that look-ma-no-hands virtuosity, and even, because he sometimes wrote so awfully (*Murphy* especially, and the Belacqua stories—why didn't someone tell him to quit?), he pandered to my pride. His creatures fleshed out the newly encountered antinomies for me, and it was through Beckett that I arrived at Joyce, Dante, Proust, Swift, even Cervantes, a wanderer discovering Troy by way of Philadelphia, I owed him a lot. He taught me patience (one needs it to read him, and that's no disparagement) and obedience, and above all he helped scrub the canvas clean: "No, no souls, or bodies, or birth, or life, or death, you've got to go on without any of that junk, that's all dead with words, with excess of words, they can say nothing else. . . ."

There was a lot of dissatisfaction in the air then with the traditional novel, I think there was, I felt it anyway, even the best of them seemed somehow irrelevant, social allegories unadaptable to the sudden dissolutions upon us, but when self-critical (not often) I supposed all that to be just part of the old generational comedy, the adolescent cutting loose from his fathers by chopping off their balls, and too easily bored by what was intelligent and difficult. But then, at Chicago, the philosopher Richard McKeon turned my restless gaze for a moment on the history of ordered discourse, and I saw, or thought I saw, that the fashion of the world was indeed changing, not only were we about to leave behind the recent age of expression, of analysis, of words and deeds, for another frantic go at the strange instable stuff we stood on, more *Weltanschauung* explorations, but in fact a whole cycle of innocence and experience, begun in the Enlightenment, was drawing to an exhausted —even frightened—close. And sure enough, the cry was abroad, philosophers asking for a New Enlightenment, theologians for a New Age of the Spirit, psychologists throwing out the old distinction of sanity and madness, in the same manner that physicists were having done with matter and energy, historians getting rid of history itself, ecologists metamorphosing all our progressive assumptions into imminent disasters, and as for the young of the sixties, it seemed to be less in their heads than in their blood.

So I was hardly surprised to find, some time later, Beckett telling Duthuit (those three little dialogues and the chapter on Murphy's three zones have become for the intrepid Beckett explorer, I'm afraid, what "The Whiteness of the Whale" chapter has been for the Melville people): "Others have felt that art is not necessarily expression." He wants no more vain efforts to extend art's repertory, this "straining to enlarge the statement of compromise," choosing instead "to submit wholly to" (imitate?) "the incoercible absence of relation . . . between the artist and his occasion." Yet, though "there is nothing to express, nothing with which to express," etc., there is still "the obligation to express": Beckett stands at the end of a collapsing era, telling us how it is ("for he had to") as the old structures sink away in the timeswamp, behaving now like an action painter—all breathless flow, process, inexplicable change ("What was that I said? It does not matter")—now like an abstract expressionist, painting absences, white on white. He undoes all our ancient notions about character, plot (history), setting ("—but to hell with all this fucking scenery," grumps Malone), and his entire opus might be thought of, from one point of view, as the relentless annihilation of "point of view." In *Texts for Nothing IV:*

> He has me say things saying it's not me, there's profundity for you, he has me who say nothing say it's not me. . . . If at least he would dignify me with the third person, like his other figments, not he, he'll be satisfied with nothing less than me, for his me. . . . His life, what a mine, what a life, he can't have that, you can't fool him, ergo it's not his, it's not him, what a thought, treat him like that, like a vulgar Molloy, a common Malone, those mere mortals, happy mortals, have a heart, land him in that shit. . . .

DON QUIXOTE has taken mortally ill. The promise of new adventures does not restore him. "I feel that I am rapidly sinking," he tells the merciless voices, "let us put aside all jesting." No longer Quixada, Quesada, Quixana, Quixote, or the shepherd Quixotiz, but now Quixano, Alonso the formerly Good ("a good man, at bottom, such a good man, how is it nobody ever noticed it?"), he calls for a witness and a scribe, and having stated his preambles and commended his soul to Heaven, he stretches his battered body to full length in the bed and says: "I shall soon be quite dead at last in spite of all. Perhaps next month. Then it will be the month of April or of May. For the year is still young, a thousand little signs tell me so. Perhaps I am wrong, perhaps I shall survive Saint John the Baptist's Day and even the Fourteenth of July, festival of freedom. Indeed I would not put it past me to pant on to the Transfiguration, not to speak of the Assumption. . . ."

I did not explore Cervantes' books in any thoroughgoing way (let's admit it, all I knew was the *Classic Comics* version of Quixote and the windmills) until poverty reduced me to teaching them at a small college four years ago, and I found my passage marked with a thousand recognitions from my life with Beckett, the impotent old clown caught up in the mad toils of earnestness ("The most cunning part in a comedy," says Don Quixote soberly, "is the clown's"), sallying forth on his decrepit vehicle to essay the impossible in the name of vanished hopes, yes, I knew him, and the wonderful rhetorical comedy, the clichés and proverbs, puns and name-games, the intransigent adherence to ludicrous strategies, the hat tricks and whimsical outdated getup, the stories-within-stories (and where was Cervantes behind all his "I's"?), the puppets and the mock heroics, the slapstick, thumpings, and hollow victories, even little consonances like Lady Pedal and the Duchess, the stampede of pigs, the penance in the wilderness, the love letters, yes, Beckett's gentlemen were all Quixotes (or vice versa), Malone especially, aha, there was the pivotal narrative, I decided, Malone was The Last Quixote, what an idea, or what was left of him anyway, now moribund and hopelessly addled, bedridden, "I have lived in a kind of coma," M/Q confesses, nothing new to report yet babbling on, three and a half centuries later. "And what can have changed him so? Life perhaps, the struggle to love, to eat, to escape the redressers of wrong." And if the invention of the Novel ("Wrong, very rightly wrong. You invent nothing. . . .") could be witnessed in the vibrant space between *Don Quixote Part I* and *Part II,* I thought so, an occasion coinciding with the commencement of this our perishing Era of what shall we call it, of Science and History let us say (if we're to believe the latter—traps everywhere!), so now was Beckett finishing the old form off in *Malone Dies,* or thus I told my classes for fear otherwise of falling silent.

More: the whole narrative trilogy, Beckett's, might be read, I went on, as a gloss on Quixote's first sally, the forgotten one, Sancho (from whom the new novel proceeds) not yet in the picture, the old boy (after a bit of foreplay with names and costumes) slipping out heroically under cover of night, clip-clopping down the road, prattling to himself in the high style, dignifying whores and sharpers, misinterpreting all the signs picked up by his stricken senses, so paralyzed by his fantasy that he has to be spoon-fed, getting heads broken and hides whipped in the cause of love and goodness (Cervantes even makes a joke along the way about the sun being hot enough "to dissolve his brains, if he had had any left"—"Perhaps it is liquefied brain," says the narrator of *The Unnamable* of the tears streaming down his cheeks), finally ending up prostrate on an open plain, the ludicrous victim of life and muleteers, rolling about helplessly, singing out gallantries from the *Abencerraje*. In similar fashion, Malone's Macmann, grow-ing restless stretched out in the rain, starts "flinging him-self from side to side as though in a fit of the fever, but-toning himself and unbuttoning and finally rolling over and over in the same direction, it little matters which," but in-stead of recitations from the Age of Romance, Macmann's oratory springs from realism and its Cartesian logic, from the Age of the Novel:

And as he rolled he conceived and polished the plan of continuing to roll on all night if necessary, or at least until his strength should fail him, and thus approach the confines of this plain which to tell the truth he was in no hurry to leave, but nevertheless was leaving, he knew it. And without reducing his speed he began to dream of a flat land where he would never have to rise again and hold himself erect in equilibrium, first on the right foot for example, then on the left, and where he might come and go and so survive after the fashion of a great cylinder endowed with the faculties of cognition and volition. And without exactly building castles in Spain for that

CERVANTES, HAPPY with the world's mechanics, cause and effect, history, logic, dutifully returns and polishes off the scene (the battle with the "gallant Biscayan") that he in-terrupts midphrase like that, but Beckett, breaking free, if free is the word, never returns to Macmann in the rain. "In his country the problem—no, I can't do it. The peasants. His visits to. I can't . . . There is a choice of images." We see the new synthesis created by Cervantes disintegrating before our eyes (Quixote's lance reduced to a crutch, a stick—"I thought I was turning my stick to the best possible account, like a monkey scratching its fleas with the key that opens its cage"—and finally a pencil stub; and when even that is momentarily lost, history itself drops out: "I have spent two unforgettable days of which nothing will ever be known . . ."), and this disintegration is partly because Beckett is absorbing his theses and antitheses in negation, not affirmation: "There at least is a first affirmation, I mean negation, on which to build." Malone is reduced to "eat and excrete . . . live and invent." The alliance of vision and scatology (as Molloy says, "dreaming and farting"), common to all revelations since John the Seer's, was for Cervantes merely one of countless consequences of his turning away from the imitation of Beauty to attempt instead the incarnation of ideas in something resembling the world of men, and he gets a lot of liberating fun out of it (though for that matter, Cervantes is still bowdlerized to this very day—the children have to be protected from Sancho filling his pants at the fulling mill in an un-Christian funk), but for Malone it has become a basic principle, and home itself for the narrator of *How It Is. Don Quixote* was a sallying forth from the confining irrelevant wrap of the Platonic spheres of Truth and Beauty into process, discovery, possibility, but in Beckett's books and plays we are caught up again in the vicious circles, digestive cycles, the nothing new ("what vicissitudes within what changelessness") of what Nathan Scott calls this "late, bad time that begins sadly and desperately [Mr. Scott is a theologian] to be spoken of as 'postmodern,' or even 'post-Christian.'" "The Beckett trilogy," Hugh Kenner writes, "takes stock of the Enlightenment, and reduces to essential terms the three centuries during which those ambitious processes of which Descartes is the symbol and progenitor . . . accomplished the dehumanization of man."

For Cervantes, at the outset of the process, the novel was a kind of new resolution, a way to get on with it in a suddenly changing world, a way to escape the darkness of the old literature, the old dead language; for Beckett, at the end, it is "mortal tedium." Beckett, writes Scott, "stands against the whole tradition in literature . . . which represents the novel as a type of genuinely empirical examination of human experience." But of course, at the same time, it is an empirical examination of human experience for all that, for though he reverses traditional novel habits, begins with death, concludes with prefaces, exposes his inventions, turns love into macrocosmic tyranny, the bizarre multiplier of human misery, dissolves character, thought, and action into the mere flow of language, it is still a faithful report from the voices, "the things one has to listen to, I say it as I hear it," news from the real world, and if "the voices, wherever they come from, have no life in them," well, that's how it is, and more empirical than most of the wishful thinking that passes elsewhere for history.

Just as much of the energy of *Don Quixote* derives from Cervantes' own nostalgia for the chivalric romances, so do Beckett's books tend to make it from page to page by the strength of his affection for old-fashioned storytelling:

> No, grave, I'll be grave, I'll close my ears, close my mouth and be grave. And when they open again it may be to hear a story, tell a story, in the true sense of the words, the word hear, the word tell, the word story, I have high hopes, a little story, with living creatures coming and going on a habitable earth crammed with the dead, a brief story, with night and day coming and going above, if they stretch that far, the words that remain, and I've high hopes, I give you my word.

But the story we get, as we're getting there in *Texts for Nothing,* is the story of the novelist cut off from his form. As Beckett's voices launch narratives, drop them, ruminate on trivia, then suddenly, as though in a twinge of conscience or terror, pick them up again, change persona and place, leap over transitions, suffer contradictions, just as abruptly become disgusted and give it all up, cry out again, hurry on, etc., the reader is dragged through all the fitful emotions (including both boredom and hysteria, or something at the edge of it, maybe the shared sensations of our times, as we move helplessly and meaninglessly toward annihilation) of the novelist's so-called creative process, only to arrive at the negative denouement that it's all been for nothing: "But my notes have a curious tendency, as I realize at last, to annihilate all they purport to record."

MAYBE THE MOST impressive thing about Beckett, in spite of all the self-mockery, is his great sense of vocation, his almost awesome obedience of that ancient instinct to listen and report, in a time when no effort of the rational or imaginative apparatus can provide us one acceptable reason for, well, for going on with life itself, much less doing it the hard way. "And indeed the silence at times is such that the earth seems uninhabited." He is like those great sculptors who spend whole lives in the relentless pursuit of some impossible quality, a glance, a gesture, a pygmalion, a leg, and who end up giving us not so much objects, as a process, humbling, archetypal, preceptive—for whatever else Beckett's art is, it is a lifelong parable on what writing itself is all about, not so much a new narrative genre or rhetorical fashion (though this may be happening, too), as a kind of eightfold path for the maker (which is all of us, after all, if we're not afraid of madness) on his way to failure, an exemplary settling down into the Self through all its pseudoselves and posturings, disguises, imaginative displacements, with no illusions, doubting even the wherewithal. Reporter, clown, and seer: he is like Hesiod's paradigmatic poet who celebrates his age, provides relief from sorrow, and serves as a prophet of religious truth. And like Don Quixote, who—having been flogged unmercifully by a gang of Yanguesans, flung over an ass, laid out on a wooden plank, busted in the face till his old jaws were bathed in blood, trampled in the ribs and thrown senseless to the floor, had his beard grabbed by a lawman and his head cracked with blows from the officer's oil lamp, poisoned himself with homemade balsam that emptied him out violently from both ends—could still, with all the dignity of a great clown, stagger away toward new adventures, reminding his disciple: "Be quiet and have patience, for a day will come when you will see with your own eyes how fine a thing it is to follow this profession."

A Home-Cooked Meal
for The Astronaut

Steve Katz

THE ASTRONAUT holds his nose by the river and watches the puffed bodies of fish drift down. They gather in eddies near the slimy banks, their nacreous underbellies scintillating in the smoky light. Up and down the river freckle-faced boys with fishing poles are weeping. He remembers the human dream he had just the night before in which there appeared to him a speckled trout, three river crabs, a pickerel, a small-mouthed bass, a yellow perch, a sunfish, a catfish, a sucker, a carp, and sixteen eels. They were all whistling a stupid protest song in a shallow pond, and when he decided to take a swim they all turned to towels, wiping him dry faster than he could get wet. "Such a ridiculous universe," he muses. "Galaxies screw it up. Stars and stuff screw up the galaxies. Planets screw up the solar systems. And then people screw up the bodies they inhabit. And then there's the gypsies, the Rosicrucians, the motorcycle gangs, meteorites, comets whizzing in long parabolas, clouds of ions, busses full of mind-blowing freaks, exploding stars, trucks out of control, the everyday vagrant person without a cent to his name. It's more than anyone can worry about." The Astronaut turns from the scene of desolation in the river to the desolate scene of the city itself. Garbage heaps. Garbagey air. Folks wander around in the garbage, kicking it up underfoot, sucking it into their lungs, kissing it into each other's mouths. The Garbage Age, not the space age, or the computer age. Garbage fills everything: the oceans, rivers, the air, garbage bunches up against the curbs and flows onto the sidewalk, garbage lies against the trunks of the last few trees, garbage gathers in doorways. People leave their buildings, arms full of garbage to drop on top of garbage pails that are already stuffed. Garbage trucks cruise by with filth leaking from their seams and haul the garbage to incinerators that burn continually, dumping the garbage smoke into the air. The threat of inundation by garbage sends men squirming off into outer space, wearing ridiculous costumes; sets men to explore deep oceans in claustrophobic bubbles; and when they fill those outposts with wastes who knows what new heights or depths they will muck up? Man has the genius for creating dumps. Only Blathinger's garbage theory of creation, The Astronaut reflects, holds the phenomenon in clear enough perspective so the prodigious quantities of garbage can be understood. His book, *Waste and Rebirth,* explains with sheaves of incontrovertible evidence his vision of the constant universe with alternating metabolic and antimetabolic eras in which the life of one era sustains itself on the garbage of the last. From that book many of the present-day garbage-worship cults originate. Blathinger himself suggests that the worship of waste is inherent in everyone in the following familiar passage from the book mentioned above: ". . . so we note that a man in a defecatorium will find it almost impossible to desist from taking a last look at his production, which he will admit smells foul, but is also disconcertingly appetizing, and it is not merely, as strict Freudians might suggest, that he is recalling his childish pride in his creation and hopes for the love of his toilet-trainer, but every man can also see through this opaque mass into his own heapie [*heapie* is the Blathingerian term for the level of the psyche he defines as being far below the subconscious, a mass of primordial waste from which all things originate, in which everything still participates, a protean dungheap, the eschatological number one, *ed.*] into the Ur-heapie, the origin of all manifestations of creation and consciousness . . ." Life persists, according to Blathinger, in a metabolic era such as the present until wastes reach cataclysmic proportions and smother all life in its own garbage, at which point everything rests for uncounted centuries until the new, antimetabolic forms appear spontaneously, an era of hydrocarbon breathers, munchers of minerals and plastics, with open sores that work like muscles, who communicate by coughing. At first The Astronaut thought the theory was just another crackpot idea until he himself began to have experiences in his travels that corroborated Blathinger. Evidence mounted in every galaxy, and his last trip capped it off, when he discovered on his brief sojourn on an otherwise barren planet, a huge mountain of lamb chops tall as the Himalayas, but discarded as if they were nothing but waste and not worth at least $1.96 a pound.

The Astronaut descends into the stench of the subway. The walls are smeared with messages in lipstick: IF YOU DON'T THINK I'M PRETTY DON'T SQUEEZE MY TIT, L.M.; THE DINOSAUR LOVES TONY P.; FREE-DOM NOW REBIRTH LATER. Three men covered with *The New York Times* are sleeping at the base of the steps, their lips fluttering against the pavement. A young cop prances nervously around them, poking at the bodies with his nightstick. He lives on Long Island. He has soft blue eyes and pale skin but for his neck that is rosy with frustration. The Astronaut pauses to observe. "Do you see these kind of bums? They'll wake up and call me a pig." The cop shrugs. The Astronaut decides to know these men. "The one on the bottom is Uncle Louie," says The Astronaut. "That one with his head on the roll of paper against the wall is Mr. Burnham Fulton Jones, and the third is Mr. Jones's faithful editor and disciple, Sidney."

The young law enforcer looks at The Astronaut and then the sleepers and scratches his head with the nightstick. "You don't know these creeps. They lie around like a bunch of bums and you look like a normal person."

"You're wrong. I know them. They're just the kind of men who sleep when they're tired."

Wrinkles sprout by the young policeman's eyes as he squints to pierce the obscurity of a strange mode of life. "You mean they got no home to go to? No beds of their own to grab a night's sleep? No wives to make them coffee? What kind of a way of life is that?"

"It's just another way," The Astronaut explains. "To these people it makes no difference if they have all the comforts in the world. If they want a sleep they take it, boom, wherever they are. They're a new kind of people. I was with Uncle Louie here once when he was swimming at Cape Cod and got tired. He feel asleep in the water and woke up nine hours later, seventeen miles out to sea. It took him eight hours to swim back and he was so tired when he got there that he fell asleep again, immediately, on the beach, and if I hadn't been luckily digging clams nearby he would have been wiped out to sea again by the tide."

"O brother," says the cop, slapping his nightstick in his palm. "Have you been handing me a load. I suggest you just move along and I'll find these freaks a comfortable cell."

A few people rush up the stairs from a train, ignoring the sleepers. "Your jails are already so crowded. Why should you arrest them? Any minute they'll wake up and leave. Will you arrest someone who's just sleeping? What for?"

"Don't give me 'what for,' " says the cop. "These creeps have got vagrancy, and you've got being a pain in the ass to a police officer, so move along and don't assemble here." The cop begins to circle the sleepers again, pushing at them with his foot. "I said for you to move along." The cop glares at The Astronaut, who doesn't seem ready to leave. "Okay, what's your line of work, mister?"

"I'm The Astronaut."

"O Christ," says the cop. "Another fruitcake. So I'm the mayor of New York City. You'd better hop into your capsule and move, Astronaut."

"Why don't you let me wake them up for you first?"

"Blast off, Astronaut, before I scrub your mission."

"Give me one chance. I need to speak with them anyway."

The officer prods a few more times without luck, and then takes off his cap and fans his face with it. "What the hell. Go ahead. What can I lose? They're not getting up for me. But I warn you not to try any of your far-out stuff when they're awake. I'm a Black Belt, and I'm not afraid to use it."

The Astronaut bends down and starts to speak to the man he has named Uncle Louie. "Wake up, Uncle Louie.

It's The Astronaut. Time to get up now. You're not supposed to be sleeping here." Uncle Louie starts to suck like a baby and then opens his eyes. "We have to wake up Mr. Jones and Sidney, too." The man stirs himself, slowly rising to his full height.

"What a whopper," says the cop. "He's a real beanpole."

"Uncle Louie is over seven feet tall," says The Astronaut, "and he's still young. He keeps on growing, and soon he'll be the tallest man in the world."

"I bet he'll still sleep in the subways like a bum."

Uncle Louie bends over to look the cop in the eye. "I sleep in the subway when I get tired in the subway. I got tired in the subway."

"The subways are filthy garbage places," the cop says. "Only the bums, the creeps, and the hippies would sleep here. Even Communists wouldn't sleep here, who don't want to work for a living."

"I beg your pardon, sir, but I should like to differ with you on several of these matters." Mr. Burnham Fulton Jones has been awakened by the argument and is meticulously stripping off the newspaper that he used to cover himself. His garments are fabulous: a carefully tailored five-button double-breasted white corduroy jacket, carefully creased narrow-legged deep-olive bell-bottoms with aquamarine pin stripes. Around his neck, between the gamboge wings of his collar, a magenta ascot made exclusively for him by Tum-Suden Designs, glows like a landing light. "It happens to be an aspect of our belief, and I'm sure had we the opportunity to speak with you it would become an aspect of yours, that it benefits one to sleep wherever the notion of sleep assails him, especially if he should find himself in a filthy place with garbage about him and vermin crawling out, because we know the filth of our origin, and from the filth you awaken reborn. You have contacted the source."

"The sauce is right. You got the sauce all over yourself, haw." The policeman laughs at his own pun out of the right side of his smirk. "Now I don't care what you guys believe, because this is a free country. I don't care where you guys came from, or what they do there when they sleep. Worship where you please, even if it's in the garbage. But don't sleep like a public nuisance. This is a free country so you guys are free to get on a train and get out of here, or go back to the street, but no more sleeping."

"You're such a fine-looking young policeman that I would hate to wake up Sidney in his wrath for you. He has been editing my life's work and is very tired. This opportunity has been his first to catch a bit of sleep. He'll be enraged."

"If you don't get him moving I'll have to advise you of your rights and then you'll get to sleep in a cell."

"You might as well get him up, Mr. Jones," says The Astronaut. "Eileen has invited all of you for dinner. Aren't you hungry?"

"Hunger is my specialty," says Burnham Fulton Jones. "Uncle Louie, we'll have to wake up Sidney, but stay out of his way."

The tall man begins to rustle the paper around Sidney with his size-24 feet. "Sidney," he sings. "Good old Sidney, wake up. We're going to have some eat, and the cop tells us to move."

"Please don't be upset, Sidney," says Burnham Fulton Jones as the newspapers begin to tumble. "This gentleman in blue is displeased that we choose to sleep where we worship. He asks us to move, so I suppose we must."

Out of the mass of paper like a mushroom from the leaves rises a fierce bald man parting his thin lips to release a growl. He glares at the cop with his one good eye; the other is made of glass with a six-pointed star for its pupil. He lifts himself from the rubbish in a long, ratty, brown tweed coat full of holes. He wears sandals cut from tires and his shirt is rotting at the collar. He salutes Burnham Fulton Jones and smiles, still growling, his mouth full of tin. "Who are you?" he asks The Astronaut.

"I am The Astronaut," he replies.

"You are fortunate. And who are you?" he asks the cop.

"You'd better just move along. I'm an officer of the law."

"Then you are the swine who interrupted my sleep," says Sidney, his growl persisting. "You awakened me prematurely, and that isn't advisable. You have cause to regret it, and your family will rue this day." Sidney swiftly draws from under his coat an enormous broadsword engraved at the hilt with the name "Heiligenschmerz," and before anyone can prevent him he lifts the sword high above his head and brings it down with terrifying swiftness on the right shoulder of the cop, cleaving the bones and splitting the young law officer in twain diagonally through the heart. The three men then rush up the stairs and down the street to the East Side.

The Astronaut bends over to catch the last few words of the bifurcated cop. "I guess that's the last time I'll ever try to wake up such a bunch of bums" is all he can manage. The Astronaut pulls shut his eyelids and leans the head back on the newspaper.

"Now I have to catch the uptown local," he whispers into a dead ear.

"You guys leave quite a mess," the man in the change booth says through his coin-hole.

"In this day and age, such terrible things happen," says an old woman changing a dollar.

"Who cares?" says the raven-haired beauty next in line, patting the curlers in her hair.

The train is packed with people on crutches and in wheelchairs, all headed for Times Square. Braces, and elbows, and knees, and prostheses jab The Astronaut from all sides. When the train pitches a little woman grabs the back of his arm with her teeth.

"Sorry, sir," she says, letting go. "Otherwise I'm helpless."

At Forty-second Street the whole crowd tries to exit, to catch the shuttle, and The Astronaut slowly loses his grip on the center pole as the mob presses on him in a clatter of crutches.

"Mister," one voice rises in his ear. "Why don't you just get out of the car for a moment so people can get by?" The Astronaut swings around, hitting the lady with his arm. "You son of a bitch," she says, lifting her crutch in the air. "I'm a cripple, but I'll brain you with my crutch."

The Astronaut grabs the crutch from her hands, breaks it in two, and tosses it across the platform. "My crutch," she screams. "You have destroyed my crutch."

"That's all right, lady," says The Astronaut. "Now you can walk good as new. Try to walk."

"I'm a helpless cripple," she screams.

"Just try to walk."

The lady takes some faltering steps and discovers her legs are sound as a colonel's. "I can walk alone. I can walk." Her voice deepens to a low tremolo. "I can jump. I can run." She disappears up the ramp after her crippled friends, without thanking The Astronaut, not that he expects to be thanked. He would rather not to have done that thing, because he prefers to go unnoticed. It was a mistake caused by the ugly human emotion of frustration. In the future he will have to control such lapses.

"You're just terrible. That was awful what you just did," says a neat little man by his side, holding a black attaché case under his arm. "The least you could have done . . ." The man frowns, but symmetrical scars on either side of his mouth extend from the corners of his mouth to just below his ears, giving him the appearance of a permanent smile. "The very least would have been for you to throw the broken pieces into the appropriate receptacle. You people come here from out of town and make our city filthy."

EILEEN NUDGES a spicy hors d'oeuvre between The Astronaut's lips as soon as he walks in the door. She has made lots of goodies: truffled pâté, beluga caviar, spicy raw kibby, all spread on flaky crackers. Though The Astronaut confuses her, she really likes him, and feels herself "getting serious" about him. He is what folks in her home town might call a "weirdo," and that makes her even fonder.

"I'm glad to see you again. We haven't been together since I quit my last job," she says.

"You quit again?" The Astronaut mumbles with his mouth full.

"It's not possible to work anymore. Nobody's competent to work anymore. I take a job and in two weeks I know more about the business than anybody else. They want me to work late, to work Saturdays, because all the starlets they hire foul everything up. I go bananas just because I can be competent in some stupid job. I don't care if the kids of America never get their Thread of Light Junior Laser Kits. I quit the job."

The Astronaut nibbles a bare cracker. "Now you'll have to hunt up a new job," he says.

"It's too late. To hell with it. I'm a changed woman. I can't find another job."

"How are you a changed woman? You've just gotten ridiculous, Eileen, since I've known you."

"It's because I know you that I'm a changed woman, and can never work again."

"What could I possibly have to do with any change in your life?"

"You don't work."

"How can you say I don't work? What I do is invisible to you, whether you know it or not."

"I know you're The Astronaut, and whatever you do doesn't seem unpleasant or difficult for you. Just because I'm a woman doesn't mean I can't do the same thing."

"That's crazy. Because you think I don't work you're never going to work again? How are you going to live?"

Eileen hands The Astronaut a last hors d'oeuvre and then flops down on the fluffy white throw rug near her couch. "I don't need to talk about it. I just want to be with you. I want to leave with you when you leave this planet."

"That's really a stupid idea. It's impossible. Do I have to explain to you that I'm not even human?"

"If we really want to, we can make it possible."

The Astronaut lies down beside her. "You are going to have to change your mind about that."

Eileen rolls onto her belly and her light cotton minidress hikes up to her waist. Her buttocks surface like a sunny shoreline. "When you eat the meal that I've cooked for you tonight you'll change your mind. You'll insist that I should come along just to cook your meals."

"You have no understanding of what happens to me when I change place. Eating is something that is done on Earth, not where I come from, and it is unlikely that it will happen again anywhere else I go. If you understood all this rightly you wouldn't want to leave."

"You left your own planet."

"You don't even know that I have a planet."

"Everybody has a planet, silly. Besides, I really like you." She kisses him on the ear. "I'm very romantic, you know, and I'm sick of living on this horrible planet. It doesn't do anything for me anymore. Everybody's so mean to everybody else, and they foul everything up. And everyone's afraid. Maybe it's no better on another planet, but at least it will be different. And we'll be together."

"Listen, you are a beautiful crazy Earth lady, but you might not be able to breathe where I go next."

"I'll take that chance, as long as we're together."

"Let's stop this craziness," The Astronaut says, and he touches her buttocks, and then leans over to kiss her posterior ruga from her thigh creases to her coccyx, which he nibbles. "You taste good."

"Then you'll certainly want to take me along to provide that special nourishment."

"It's delicious being an Earthman," says The Astronaut. Eileen rolls over to kiss his face. "This is the last hors d'oeuvre you get." She plugs his mouth with her tongue, and then she starts to undress him and stroke his sex organs. She has begun to like the buzzing sound he makes whenever his cock is erect. It's like a hive of bees, or a massage machine, and his cock has a quality of heat she has never felt in herself before, and a kind of peristaltic expansion and contraction. Her vagina runs like solder and she comes and comes. "There's no one else like you inside me, peculiar and warm and active. It's like I'm blushing all through me. It's like being fucked by God, I mean it. I hope I make you feel good."

"There's no way for me to translate what I feel for you. Feeling itself is new to me."

"What a nice thing to say," she says. "Now let's eat like crazy."

"Okay, but you'll have to promise to remember that you're from Earth, Eileen, and I'm The Astronaut."

"And so you'll never know what it means to be a woman." She gives his cock a last caress and then straightens up to shake the wrinkles from her dress.

She has set the table elegantly for the two of them on a lovely rose-damask tablecloth, with the amber glassware she has taken from her mother's home, and the stainless-steel settings of Finnish design. The candlesticks are a delicate blue-green earth glaze pottery, as are the compotes and casseroles, and for the centerpiece she has set up a tiny bonsai black pine. A bottle of Château d'Yquem sauterne, vintage 1934, rests in the silver wine cooler by The Astronaut's place, and on the table a bottle of Saint-Christoly 1964 in a wicker basket. The Astronaut remarks on the thirty years' difference between the wines.

"I quite like the younger red," says Eileen, "though the old sauterne has an immense reputation. We'll have him with the asparagus, the soup and fish, but you can open the other and let it breathe until the veal."

Just think about life on Earth, The Astronaut thinks as he settles down and pops the corks. All the different kinds of wine, with certain nuances every year. And you have a palate to taste it, and nostrils to sniff it, such inventions to abstract taste from the tedious business of life-maintenance. A guy can meditate on taste alone. What a blessing is the whole battery of human senses, with the mind's capacity to abstract sensation from function, to delight in it, so being can appreciate itself. That happens only on Earth. Eileen can remember The Astronaut's sexual specialties without the fuddlement of procreation. She can tantalize herself with it, ready herself to snatch up each instant. Yet she meets her first Astronaut and wants to leave the whole kaboodle behind. What a curiosity. The Astronaut wishes there were some way to communicate the pleasures he is learning in the uses of flesh, of seeing, hearing, touching, smelling, feeling in the heart, pleasures he has found nowhere else in the universe, and never hopes to find, even in those realms of fulgent ecstasy to which he has been promised entrance once his mission is complete.

Eileen carries in two plates of tender, ivory-hued asparagus, laced with a mild vinaigrette. "This is the groovy 'Bergstrasse Spargel,'" she says. "You can't get better asparagus than what they grow between Heidelberg and Darmstadt. Once a year the little grocery store down the street manages to get a few pounds of it. He's German. He sells it by the stalk to his best customers."

"It's miraculous," says The Astronaut, lifting a white stalk in his asparagus tongs.

"Why don't you pour the sauterne?" Eileen suggests.

The taste of the fine vintage, with its sweet edge, follows the asparagus over his palate just as a pretty young girl follows onto the dance floor the handsome boy she has been hoping would ask her to dance all through the evening of her first night at a discotheque. She never thought he would ask her, and now suddenly he has. Will she dance like a nymph, or will she turn out to be a stumblebum? The question need never have been asked. The sauterne and asparagus are a wedding.

Softness and peace settle on them in the room and the dimpled angels of appetite enmesh them in webs of smiles. "I feel as if we're already going off somewhere together, this is so strange and nice here, and so quiet. I love to cook delicious meals for someone I care about. I hope we never have to leave each other."

The Astronaut can't stop smiling. He has found no way to control the mischievous little emotions you get on Earth, that send the body off into unpredictable gestures: smiles, eye blinks, brow wrinkles, sweeps of the arm, jerks of the leg. "You're being too good to me, Eileen."

"I want to keep on being good to you in your spaceship, wherever it goes."

"You are going to have to get over your primitive notions about space travel, and who can do it, and how it's done."

"The only notion I have about it is you." Eileen clears the asparagus plates and rushes back to the kitchen, leaving The Astronaut with pearly sensations of well-being. He hears her humming in the kitchen above the whirr of the blender, and then she reappears with a small tureen set in a bowl of crushed ice, which she places in front of The Astronaut, and hands him a silver ladle. "The iced avocado soup," she says, with obvious pride. "An actress friend gave me the recipe. She swears by it, and I only hope I have lived up to it."

The Astronaut ladles the soup into two shallow bowls and passes one to Eileen just as the doorbell rings. "Who else is coming?" he asks.

"No one. Don't be ridiculous. I wouldn't ask anyone else. We can pretend we're not here."

"Okay," says The Astronaut, and they both sip a little of the cold, creamy yellow-green soup. It feels like plush in the mouth and stings like a whisper. The knocking at the door persists, increasing in enthusiasm.

"I can't stand it. I'll have to go tell them what I think." Eileen folds her napkin next to her plate and goes to the door. The Astronaut stares at the droplets of water condensed on the shallow bowl. "They say they're friends of yours," Eileen says, coming back worried.

"Who are they?"

"They sure are funny looking. I've never seen them before. They told me you invited them."

The Astronaut gets up from his soup and goes to the door. At first glance he doesn't recognize the men, but then he does. "He's here. He said he'd be here," shouts one of them, whom The Astronaut remembers as Sidney. "Waddaya know and waddaya say and waddaya mean and how the hell are ya? We finally got here," says Uncle Louie, who stoops down to get in through the low doorway.

"Please accept our apologies for the tardiness. As you can well imagine from the nature of our parting earlier today we had much to delay our arrival. We were exceedingly grateful for your invitation and after much cogitation decided that if we don't come after all it would be tantamount to a personal insult," says Mr. Burnham Fulton Jones. He steps into the room, dressed to the hilt in a pale velvet cutaway morning coat, his legs cased in narrow pants of a rich umber flannel, that sets off a glistening blue satin shirt with frilled front; on his feet, lightly buffed moccasins of soft gray ostrich, and he wears a curled auburn hairpiece with a few locks teasing his ears. Sidney has shaved what little hair was left on his temples, and sports a fake black moustache. He has exchanged his ratty coat for a long black cape, and has set a strange moiré pattern in his empty eye socket. Uncle Louie is wearing tights stuffed with newspaper under a waiter's red jacket he has found, and he looks like a figure to be burned in effigy.

"It's good good good to see you again." Burnham Fulton

Jones takes a hand of The Astronaut in both his own. "I was sure you wouldn't be miffed if we took the liberty to bring along a few of our friends to share our good fortune, and to meet you, our new friend. We even thought to bring along enough food to provide for ourselves and make a party of it." Sidney shoves the door open and lets in the fetid, grimy rabble of the streets that nobody loves. They drag with them some garbage cans full of steamy, putrid stuff, and plastic bags full of sodden trash. These are the exiles in our midst, the tainted ones, the maggots, men and women smeared with filth, drink-stench, vomit, and excrement, the glorious dregs, limbless mutes toted around in sacks of greasy burlap by men with swollen eyes and running sores who scream at us and drool on us and we refuse to notice them; some cripples on splintering crutches, or strapped to dollies, pushing themselves along with their digitless wrists. The feculent mob squeezes into the room each with a bit of swill for the party. They snort at their friend, The Astronaut. Gray is their color, gray their race, and their future is gray as their hands. They bring to the throats of Eileen and The Astronaut the unquenchable odor of the streets thick as incense. These are people you pass on the way to the theater, or to the dinner party, their hands extended. They seem to have no eyes. They are sheer population in your dreams. Your children imitate them, knowing the truth. They once were the parents, the doctors, oceanographers, first lieutenants, actuaries, pilots, programmers, stenographers, stock-car racers, artists, conservationists, and now they are united in the mystery of filth, massive poverty, they have let go of everything down to the skin.

"What are these creatures doing here? Who are they?" Eileen whispers fearfully in The Astronaut's ear.

"These are the people of your city," says The Astronaut. "You see them every day. You work around them. You should remember."

"I don't know them. I don't want them in my house. They're the swill, the garbage of the Earth."

"Amen to that," says Burnham Fulton Jones, and most of the group grunts in response.

"Are you the leader of this group?" Eileen asks the one man who looks respectable to her.

"Of course not. There's no leader. Here we are, your friends."

Eileen pushes her face into The Astronaut's shoulder. "Such a stench. How will we stand the smell? They'll ruin our dinner. Please have them go away."

Sidney swings open the wings of his cape to reveal his prodigious arsenal. "We'll just stay here and amuse ourselves. You've got such a nice place, nothing to be ashamed of. You don't have to entertain us. You're being the perfect hostess." Sidney bows.

Eileen starts to laugh and weep like a woman to whom something wonderful has just happened. The crowd is flaked out all over her apartment. Three women whose faces look like they've been mashed into the sidewalk lick off their fingers that they have dipped in the avocado soup. They empty bags of garbage on her table and feel around in it for tidbits to stuff in the mouths of their red-eyed kids. "A silent butler," one man with a huge wen on his neck exclaims, and he empties a plastic sack full of gray-green slop on her stereo turntable, yanks the wires out, and spins the mess on his lap, slurping up fistfuls and licking his lips. An obese woman dressed in a rotting tent sits down on the furry throw rug by the couch and sorts through the garbage the others dump around her from the cans. "This is good stuff. This is bad stuff," she says, making two heaps. "Great stuff," says a dwarf who approaches her. He looks like a moving wart. He pulls open the fat woman's tent flap to expose her pulpy, greasy breasts, and pours the remains of the Château d'Yquem he has found in the wine cooler down her cleavage, and thrusts his face down between the breasts to lap up the flow. The fat woman unzips his fly, flips out his cock, and jerks him off between wads of white bread.

The Astronaut holds Eileen's head against his chest. "We were having such a good dinner," she whimpers. "Now everything has gone wrong."

"Good old Astronaut buddy," says the huge Uncle Louie. "Now everything is okay, normal. You know what I mean. I don't express myself well, but this is great."

Eileen suddenly leans back and starts to beat on The Astronaut's chest. "You come to the Earth and these are the only kinds of friends you can show me. These are the people you want to associate with."

"They're just Earth people. Why should I care?"

"Oh shit, my god." Eileen pushes away from him and rushes into her kitchen. The Astronaut follows. "My poached sole," she cries. "My veau milanaise." Burnham Fulton Jones is in the kitchen, emptying the pan of fish into a large sack of food scraps. "This is going to be exquisite," he says. "Perfect food." He heads for the veal that lightly simmers on the stove. "Hands off the veal," shouts Eileen, grabbing him by the belt.

"Don't worry," says Burnham Fulton Jones. "We'll all partake. We're your guests, but we'll help distribute the food."

Eileen catches the meat just before he drops it into his sack, and after a brief tug of war it rips. The well-dressed man shakes his head. "I've never seen a hostess behave like this. Your indiscretion shocks me, mamselle, and in front of our friend, The Astronaut. What opinion can he possibly have of us?" He drops his scrap of meat into the bag and leaves the kitchen.

"Here, taste it." Eileen hands The Astronaut a portion torn off the scrap she has managed to save. "Taste it. It would have been quite good. My butcher manages to find young veal." She shoves a piece into her own mouth. The Astronaut looks at his piece and smiles. Eileen is about to cry again. "What are you laughing at? Is that what you call cosmic laughter? What do you learn in outer space, how to be a stone? Don't you have any feelings?"

"When you get mad you get close to the truth," The Astronaut says. "But remember that this is here and now. You have to accommodate."

"You talk nonsense," Eileen sobs. "Leave my house. Get out. Just leave me alone."

"Are you sure? You'll be sorry tomorrow."

"Just get going."

The Astronaut shoves his way through the slobs to get to the door. A man sits on a stool near the entrance with a notebook on his knee, jotting down his "aperçus." "You ought to use a camera," The Astronaut advises. "You can never catch the flavor of this scene using mere language." He drops down the steps two at a time, and rushes into the street to stick out his tongue. A bright patter of rain falls on the tongue, rinsing it clean, tasting sweet.

Ego Loss

Daryl Hine

FOR STEVEN M. L. ARONSON

AT A little less than a year and 70 lbs.
A dog named Ego is being mistranslated
to out-of-sight New York from lacustrine Chicago
in a laminated case marked Air Freight Cargo
whose aperture is cruelly barred and grated
against the barks with which the terminal resounds.

All the air is filled with inarticulate noise,
for soon to be airborne Ego is far from faring well.
The minute you turn your back the dog complains.
His kennel—the regulation American cell—
is inadequate as home; no wonder he destroys
it before our eyes: Ego, everywhere in chains.

Psychoanalysis and the keeping of pets teach us
that more than anything else we want to eat mother;
though this is not possible in Ego's hermetic cabin.
Ego and I do not have to like one another
in order for reality to reach us
reciprocally. We must make each other happen

Or die. Now Ego has no idea where he is going.
The curiosity of his kind no more than courage
is necessary to endure this voyage
above the Midwest waste and moribund Lake Erie
in the bowels of an all too fallible Boeing.
Le voyage ennuie, and Ego soon grows weary

of his trip. The unseen earth comes up to meet him
at the end of the jet-propelled *descensus Averni.*
Once debarqued, there is Sibyl to greet him.
Ego will awaken from his journey
a continent away, oblivious of the city
where I abide, the other side of pity.

The Victor Dog

James Merrill

FOR ELIZABETH BISHOP

Bɪx to Buxtehude to Boulez,
The little white dog on the Victor label
Listens long and hard as he is able.
It's all in a day's work, whatever plays.

From judgment, it would seem, he has refrained.
He even listens earnestly to Bloch,
Then builds a church upon our acid rock.
He's man's—no—he's the Leiermann's best friend,

Or would be if hearing and listening were the same.
Does he hear? I fancy he rather smells
Those lemon-gold arpeggios in Ravel's
'Les jets d'eau du palais de ceux qui s'aiment.'

He ponders the Schumann Concerto's tall willow hit
By lightning, and stays put. When he surmises
Through one of Bach's eternal boxwood mazes
The oboe pungent as a bitch in heat,

Or when the calypso decants its raw bay rum
Or the moon in *Wozzeck* reddens ripe for murder,
He doesn't sneeze or howl; just listens harder.
Adamant needles bear down on him from

Whirling of outer space, too black, too near—
But he was taught as a puppy not to flinch,
Much less to imitate his bête noire Blanche
Who barked, fat foolish creature, at King Lear.

Still others fought in the road's filth over Jezebel,
Slavered on hearths of horned and pelted barons.
His forebears lacked, to say the least, forbearance.
Can nature change in him? Nothing's impossible.

The last chord fades. The night is cold and fine.
His master's voice rasps through the grooves' bare groves.
Obediently, in silence like the grave's
He sleeps there on the still-warm gramophone

Only to dream he is at the première of a Handel
Opera long thought lost—*Il Cane Minore.*
Its allegorical subject is his story!
A little dog revolving round a spindle

Gives rise to harmonies beyond belief,
A cast of stars. . . . Is there in Victor's heart
No honey for the vanquished? Art is art.
The life it asks of us is a dog's life.

Daddy

Harold Ober

FOR HER he would do anything: climb the highest mountain, swim the deepest sea. But he does what he can: bends pipe cleaners into funny animals, plays peekaboo behind the living room sofa, flaps hand-shadows between any handy light and wall. For her? Anything—at least, peppermint-stick ice cream cones, salt-water taffy, a toy telephone, Mister Potato-Head, finger paints, a xylophone. He tells her stories featuring people with outlandish names like Biskerspiltz and Fruister in which the villain carries a No Trespassing sign and ends up slipping on the ice and falling on his fat fanny. Or else he sings one of his loony songs, "I Wish I Was a Rhinocerarius," and rolls his eyes. When she laughs he is so happy he laughs with her, hugging her small shoulders, inspired to an imitation of a ping-pong ball perhaps or a dialogue between his thumbs. He would go to any lengths to make her happy, hear the tinkle of her laughter, see her face radiant with delight. And why not? He is her Daddy, a brand-new, unbroken-in Daddy with red hair and blue eyes, able to imitate the silverware lying down for supper or make music from the inside of his cupped hands. He is a man of a thousand voices, a thousand faces, a million surprises. Sometimes when she isn't looking he comes up behind her on all fours and hoarsely whispers "rrrrrrrROAST BEEF!" and wraps her up in his arms like a grizzly bear. He would do everything to hear her call him Daddy (buy her a tricycle, fly to the moon) . . . but it's always the same; even when she says "Daddy," he is certain she means it not as his own name but as the job Daddy that was there before he was. He is the new Daddy come to replace the old one who broke down and died. Or he is another compensation provided by the insurance company. Or worst of all, he is—leper, spastic, mongoloid—her stepfather.

Sometimes at breakfast it is the two of them alone— mother still sleeping—and he looks up from his grapefruit to watch her buttering a muffin or biting with little teeth into a triangle of toast. He smiles to see her there; she is wrapped in a too-big terrycloth bathrobe; the sun is in her lap. And just as he is about to walk two fingers over to her plate for a visit she lifts her head and he sees her eyes gray and opaque, their focus lost in thought, gazing not at him but through him as if he were not there, or ever there. It chills him, and in that one instant all the jokes, all the jugglery and all the foolery, are just so many raisins in the palm of his hand. He is jealous of her secrets. While she lets this new Daddy entertain, he worries, is she recalling her father, the real one, who shared in her conception and fathered her for her first five years? He begins to despair, watching as from a window. What can a step-father expect (what does he have a right to expect) beyond accommodation at best? How can he hope to ever get close to her mind? "Hey," he says across the jam jars, nabbing her attention, "watch this," and he balances a butter knife on the end of his little finger.

LYING in bed with his wife, he is going to make love, his hand already feeling the slope of her hips and belly, wrist-watch ticking on the night table behind his head. They have left off talking about the day, about Carolyn and how he spoils her, about how it is compared to how it was. She is the alluring widow now, and he is Eric the Red, and they are going to make love until they fall asleep. She thinks of herself as a vamp, taken in a breathless moment by a Byronic lothario in a parlor scene. She struggles at first, then swoons on the divan, exposing one white shoulder. He imagines himself as a brute, a reeking barbarian, sinister at first and then raging, forests growing from his legs and arms, mere tendons becoming sinews. He is ravaging her, a maid, against the earth, stripping off her rustic garments in violent shreds. Although they are un-aware of each other's fantasies, she enjoys being dominated, feeling his bristling body against hers; for him she is like a rich French dessert. At the end they are both exhausted; they lie together, his arm flung over her back, her leg pale beside his.

In the early morning dimness he wakes with a start and blinks at the blue still shapes of the room. For some seconds he is still disoriented, groping at the vague cobweb of the dream he just woke from. He hears nothing more than his wife's sibilant breathing and the relentless ticking of his watch. What woke him? He tries to re-enter his dream, but there is not even a door now. He turns heavily on his side away from his wife and the movement is just enough to alter her breathing from mouth to nose. Now he hears what interrupted his dream: it is Carolyn talking in her sleep, the muttered words low and unintelligible, muffled, just reaching his ear through the wall behind his head.

HAL'S TOY AND HOBBY SHOP. Before he bought it he stood there for fifteen minutes, leaving damp breath spots on the window glass. It had an honest, antique look among the dolls lying bloated and idiotic around it. What he liked was the detail. Brown-shuttered windows, green shrubs, a red chimney gable-high, were painted on its yellow tin sides with metallic clarity. And there were certain considerations that moved him—a coiled green hose, a flat pie on the kitchen windowsill, even rose bushes and trellis—cartoons, of course, but so meticulous! He angled to see the inside of that side wall. Best of all was the interior: five pigeonholes showing two bedrooms and a bathroom upstairs and a living room and kitchen downstairs, each with its own wall-painted books, or sink, or fireplace, or cupboard, plus tiny plastic furniture pieces like a yellow bed (double), blue bed, purple sofa, white stove, brown tub, red kitchen table (with four fingernail-size red chairs) . . . He was getting excited. There was even a *stairway* revealed by what was supposed to be a door partly ajar on that dividing panel between the kitchen and living room. They didn't leave out a thing. He grinned at the "shingled" black saddle roof, the gables with attic windows, the oval rugs, an integrated shower stall, even radiators. He nodded at the way the windows looking out coincided with the windows looking in.

Ten minutes of cramped fascination with these new facts and he knew he would buy it. Savoring that knowledge he straightened up and indulged five minutes more in owner's privilege. His secret was that after swallowing it all down with the feeding eye of a window-shopper he would imminently walk right into the toy shop and claim it as his own. But not really his, of course. He smiled crookedly, calculating Carolyn's reaction when she saw it. He would say, "By the way, a big orange rabbit was here to see you today. I told him you were out and he said, 'Vell, vouldjoo be so kind as to give her dis package pliz vit mine best vishes. Tell her Benny der Bunny vas here on a zocial call.'" Then he would tell her he left the strange package in her room, on the floor, and there it would be waiting for her. He could imagine her face when she saw it, like a bright button. She would throw her arms around his knees and say, "Thanks, Daddy!" and his wife Marbie would be standing at the door, shaking her head and smiling. His eyes were closed. He was smiling.

A NOTE IN HIS WIFE'S HAND waiting for him on the foyer table says: Your girls are out shopping. Be back at three about. Love, Marb. "Your girls," he repeats ironically. My girls. He pitches his coat on the bench under the barometer. His voice is the only living noise in the house and he uses it like a little rubber flyback ball, now flicked out to the length of its elastic string, now smacked back against the paddle and dangling. "Time is of the essence!" he shouts, treading the dense carpet in the living room with suede shoes. "De ezzenz!" He has the Lewjohn box still tucked under his arm (not very heavy) and he is pacing away his needling disappointment before he undertakes to put it together. "'Wait a minute,' I says. 'Don't I get the one in the window?' 'That's for display,' he says. 'Oh, sure,' I says." Which gives me two, or, no, one and three quarters hours. "*L'essence!*" But then there's the *surprise,* don't forget, and from *me,* not Benny the Bunny. "And don't forget de inztructions inzide. Zo zimble even a child can do it." He shakes the Lewjohn box. Naturally, it would have been easier for him preassembled, but don't forget it will be a labor of love, he insists, and you will

feel you have invested more than your money, *nicht war?*
"Oh, make hay, Mike!" He bounds upstairs, loose pieces in
the Lewjohn box sliding back.

Her bedroom is next to theirs, their beds sharing the
same wall so that he is up at her first whimper to dispel
nightmares, settle tummy aches, exorcise spooky noises.
It is a girl's room, pink and breezy and full of daylight from
the west window, whose white curtains fill in breezes like
sails. Dumpy dolls and stuffed bears and tigers are sitting
on her bed in a row and there are more bears on the pink
walls, plus ducks and pigs and merry-go-rounds; Japanese
paper butterflies hang from the ceiling on colored strings.
There is also a cuckoo clock, a McGraw-Hill children's
calendar (this month with a picture of Rikki-Tikki-Tavi
the mongoose and Nag the cobra), a blue window seat
that contains her games, toys, and coloring books, a
round mirror on the wall against her bed, and on the floor
an old pale-blue rug with rings of roses. Entering, he
hunches in an old doorway reflex (adolescent stealing into
his mother's boudoir?). He feels oversized and shabby,
like a telephone repairman. The dolls seem to be staring
at him. The ceiling seems only inches above his head.
Lewjohn box under his arm, he stalks oafishly for a few
minutes, about eight foot four and three hundred pounds.

He tucks her in here at night, yes, and comes to her
call, but at night it's different. Things are settled, anchored,
all secure. The colors aren't in motion. The tigers are back
to felt and stuffing. Daylight makes it less certain; the
window admits an animus from the outside. Under his foot
the rug could squeal in pain, around his head the butterflies could fly at him in a rage. In the mirror his face is
slightly alien. Meanwhile, the room could be forming an
opinion of him. He can't be sure. There is an essence
somehow, probably in the cuckoo clock. The dolls might
speak at any moment.

The label reads "Lewjohn Co., Boston, Mass." in small
black type on the glossy white box like a cipher or an
anagram. Notch's Bowels Soon Jam? Jaws Blotch On
Mooses? Low Joes Snatch Bosoms? He is feeling anxious.
"Lewjohn Company!" he blurts to dispel the cryptography.
There is a job to do. He is on his knees, picking at the tape

with his fingernails. Probably a merger of Lewis and Johnson, surnames, or Lewis and John, first names. He can see an engraving of the two brothers or partners, Lewis with a full beard, John with muttonchops, both wearing wing collars and watch chains, walking an inspection tour of their Boston bicycle factory. Says Mr. Johnson, "How do ye think, Mr. Biskerspiltz?" Replies Mr. Lewis, "It's the sound of industry, Mr. Fruister." Anyway, the top is loose. He lifts it off.

The brand-new metal sections are stacked like cards. At first he is disarmed by the parts because he is so familiar with the whole. Does one equal the other? Naturally it has to be put together. Still, this isn't *specifically* what he saw in the window of Hal's toy shop. Not yet, anyway. It wasn't this "Factory-Fresh!" he explains to his audience, the dolls and bears. The furniture is another shiny product, colors squared together in another cardboard box. The painted-on rose bushes don't move him now to transcend their cartoons. He guffaws. The funny thing is, it looks so archaic, in spite of that factory-fresh. It suggests somehow the time of a general store with barrels full of Turkish taffy, horehound drops, and nigger babies. The question is, Will she know what to do with it? Well, they have an instinct for these things, he believes. Instinctively, they all want to play house, play mommy.

"Instructions . . ."

HE IS BUILDING the dollhouse. The parts are beginning to make sense now. He is absorbed in folding Lug H into Slot H and fitting the roof on the second-floor ceiling. Ten minutes ago the cuckoo clock pronounced two o'clock while he was joining the two roof halves, lug to slot, and he heard it only peripherally and even so it meant only the time to him—that is, probably an hour more or less before his two girls (ha! ha!) are due back. Meanwhile, lying on his stomach on the rug, working from his elbows, he has erected the whole back wall, *both* side walls, the roof (a triumph!), and after he finishes joining the roof to the second-floor ceiling, he will have only to insert the mid-floor-ceiling (three floors on one side, two ceilings on the other) before dealing with the last thing he will have to deal with, namely, the rooms. The instruction book (imprinted with the same Lewjohn signature, Boston, Mass.) explains how there is one lug for each slot and thus walls can be joined to each other, to floors, to ceilings, ceilings to roof, and roof to walls as long as there is a lug to bend into a slot. Lugs and slots are paired alphabetically: Lug A to Slot A, Lug B to Slot B, Lug C to Slot C. . . . It is such a perfect fit, like lacing a shoe, and the best feeling is pairing the right lug with its slot and slowly bending it until you can feel it through—attached. The next-best feeling is the surprise of suddenly seeing the larger relationship of walls and floors and ceilings that comes quite separately, almost coincidentally, from joining the lugs and slots. He will pause after fifteen minutes' absorbed fitting and there will be the back wall, brown-shuttered living room windows, the old garden hose in its bracket, the pie cooling on the kitchen window . . . ! Where did all that come from? Modestly, "I was just following the alphabet." Meanwhile a house is going up. What a contractor! Him? The best in the business.

He imagines himself as a hard-hatted contractor, yellow-shirted in the eagle sun, directing the operations. This house is no easier and no harder than any of the others he's done. His motto is "No house ever built itself," and he always works closely with the architect. The foreman is more or less an incompetent, but there never was a foreman he was satisfied with. At least the job's getting done. Who's on Lug D? He shouts to the men on the gable: "Are you sure that lug is tight? I don't want to see any of that slot!" The men scramble, but they know he's pretty well pleased with the job. It would be hard to fault them on this one; those lugs are sound as dimes. He spits in the sand. He's never missed a contract deadline yet, and he's not about to spoil his record on this one. "I want a check on the ridge of that roof!" he tells the foreman, and the foreman grins because this is the fifth check he's made on that roof today. He's a goddam perfectionist, thinks the foreman to himself, but you have to admire a guy with a safety record like his. So the roof is checked again, and of course the lugs are sound as dimes and there is absolutely no sign of the slot. "Listen, you men, I want this house solid as a dollar by three o'clock!" he shouts, but the men know he's satisfied, and they know they'll give the old lug-pusher his house by three. They seem to guess that this job is something special. The foreman knows more. He knows this house is a present for the old governor's little girl, Carrie. He gives him a wink as if to say, "Don't worry about a thing, Mr. Lewjohn. You're gonna give her a house that she'll love you for. This is a house that's gonna have your name written all over it. This is a house that you can bank your reputation on. This is a house that she can feel safe in as long as she lives. This is a house . . ."

He is inserting that crucial piece, the mid-floor-ceiling. He slips it into a groove going the width of the three walls, and suddenly he has two floors where before there were none defined. It becomes more intimate now: he is making living quarters, prior to making rooms. Before he was only concerned with the outside, but now his attention is forced within, to the consideration of living space, the oval rugs, the bookcases, the shower stall, the cupboards, and, pretty soon, the furniture. How much time now? Forty minutes? He shifts on his side, sitting on his leg. (Rikki-tikki-tavi. "Rikki-tikki-tikki-tikki . . . Rikki-tikki-tikki-tikki . . . Rikki-tikki-tikki-tikki . . . Rikki-tikki-tavi!" Rudyard Kipling starting his car on a cold morning.) *Peering into the house, who is this man?* Now he slips in the room panels, one by one, into their own grooves in the tin floors, the ceilings, and the back wall. One by one, he makes a room. Master bedroom (hanky-panky!), bathroom (P. U.!), and the son's room. One becomes two and then two becomes three, and then downstairs the living room and the kitchen, for relaxing and eating. Go, Ace, you're in the home stretch. Look at this thing, this dollhouse. It's all ready for the furniture! Hey! Ha! Remember Hal's Hobby Shop? It's almost exactly like the one in the window! See—and you wanted a preassembled one.

"Hey I got a furniture order for family name Lewjohn? Sign here. Your receipt. Okay, we'll start with the living room. Charlie, gimme a hand with this couch." And they move it in, back it into that living room, the family bouncing around like silly people. . . . He is feeling dizzy, the pace is getting a little too fast, he is finishing this house a little too soon. Slow down, slow down. It's only two-thirty. But he still has the furniture to put in. A whole inventory, in fact: 1 sofa (purple), 2 easy chairs (green), 1 TV set (brown) (color?), 1 table (red), 4 chairs (red), 1 stove (white), 1 refrigerator (white), 1 double bed (yellow), 1 bureau chest (brown), 1 desk (black), 1 bathtub (pink), 1 single bed (blue), and 1 dresser (brown).

Operating from the elbows again, he invades the living room first. The sofa is a tiny thing between his fingers; his whole hand is actually crawling inside the living room. A Hand! Eeek! The Hand! Holding a sofa! Drop it! Where did they go? Must have fled to the bedroom! Fay Wray is up there, unaware, lying naked as a bug on the big yellow bed, UNAWARE! (He puts the double bed in hastily and then) then, the fingers are creeping, a wilderness of red hair between the knuckles! There she is, doesn't see him until—too late! Eeek! The Hand! He's got her! Nude? No, remember that scene no one was allowed to see, when he spirited her away to his cave and sat on the terrace dangling his mighty legs and began to flick—away—her garments—bit—by bit—little scraps of her dress flicked away and whisked down the draft until pretty soon she had hardly anything on—but just before he flicked away the last (clothes being a novelty to *him*, don't forget!), they were interrupted by a screaming pteranodon! The Hand Strikes Again! Arr, he knocked over the sofa. What else goes in there? TV set, easy chairs. Okay, the hand roams around on two fingers, the rest tucked behind, like coattails.

"Nice living room you got here, har har har!" Looking out the back window—"Nice view, har har har!" Ah, the kitchen . . . Bearing a refrigerator (careful with that . . .), a stove (oof!), next trip, the table and one, two, three, four chairs.

"Whew, sure do work up an appetite, har har har! What's for lunch?" The hand prowls, "Anything in the fridge? The cupboards? What, no food!" Just for that, the Hand goes into a rage, knocking over chairs, knocking over the table, knocking over the refrigerator. Crrrrash! The Hand at large!

THERE IT IS—on the roof! The Hand is wounded, climbing to the very ridge of the roof, knuckles heaving, fingers sprawled out over the rough black shingles. Oooo, look how the skin wrinkles over the joints, and under those nails—ugh—what's that crud? Yes, we've made a crucial decision: we'll buzz it! Rmmmmmmm . . . You can already hear them coming up over the horizon. Six of them, in formation. The Hand scrabbles on the roof, fingers flailing in panic.

"This is it, Hand! Rmmmmmmm," the first plane dips.

"Stay out of range of those fingers, dammit, but get in *firing* range. Look out! The Hand . . . those fingers reaching . . . quick, open fire before it . . . AAAAGH . . ."

"Oh, I can't look, that twisted wreckage, how awful!"

But The Hand is hit, bleeding from new wounds! It is definitely in a weakened state, blood welling up under the fingernails and oozing off the sides of the roof like tar. Painfully it rolls over on its back for a moment, fingers curling and uncurling like a dying roach, those mysterious whorls and lines—what do they mean?—the fingers bent just above the nails. Yes, The Hand isn't long for this world.

"Look out, Hand! You're a goner now!" Rmmmmmmm, two planes part in the sky, coming from two directions! "Hand, you've had it, you haven't got a dying chance!" Oh, the agony as The Hand rears up, feebly trying to fend them off, and then, "Rikki-tikki-tikki-tikki-tikki-tikki-tikki-tikki-tik!" Got him! Punctured in the artery! The blood comes in a river. The planes dive in low to finish it off, riddling it in a hundred places, but the last wound was mortal. The Hand is slipping now, clutching at the ridge of the roof with the last dying strength in its fingers, but it cannot hold. It slides. It falls. The Hand is no more.

"It wasn't the planes that killed The Hand, gentlemen; it was beauty, beauty killed the beast. . . ."

The last of the furniture is in the bedrooms, bright and colorful as gumdrops. That isn't the best arrangement perhaps, but she can change it around to her taste. So, the dollhouse is finished. Ready for occupancy. Hard to believe. His hand is lying in the living room, drumming fingers on the rug. How about a last quick tour? No, too tired. Think I'll just lie here on the rug, for a few more minutes anyway. What time is it? No clock in here, but it must be about time for her to get back. Any minute now, I'd say. Will she be surprised. You'd better get up, big fellow. You'd better get out of this room. It isn't your house, you don't even belong in here. Come on, UP. Still, it feels good to just lie here on the rug. Aren't I entitled to a little . . . The door! It's Goldilocks! Where to hide?? Quick—upstairs!

LYING IN BED with his wife, he is going to make love, his hand already traveling over her thighs, wristwatch ticking on the night table behind his head. They have left off talking about the day. She is Goldilocks and he is the grizzly bear and he has just surprised her in his bed, so now she's going to have to pay the penalty for trespassing. He is through fooling around. He has her thoroughly worked up now, wriggling underneath his mighty ursine loins. She grabs desperately at his shoulders: fat chance! Even now he is raping her, surging deeper and deeper, faster and faster, until she cries out. Cries again. Scream as loud as you want, Goldilocks. The bear is into you, the bear is into you, the bear is into you, the bear is into you, the bear is into you, the bear is into you, the bear is into you, the bear is into you . . .

Ending

Hilma Wolitzer

THE WAY IT WAS, I didn't love anybody. Not even Ezra. I looked down at him in his bath, dispassionate about the soft pink hills of his knees rising from the silvered water.

I don't love you, kiddo, I thought, and I poured the shampoo into the whorl of hair on top of his head. Maybe I could have loved a more conventional child, aptly named Scott or Michael or David, a boy without Ezra's secret wheezing allergies, without his straight and penetrating glance. The average American boy, I thought, *drops* his eyes when you look at him, and so prepares for the evasiveness he will use when he grows up and screws around.

I didn't really love Gene then either. I was possessive about him. I was manic; I wouldn't give him up to Bonnie or anyone. But it was hard to concentrate on *love*, on the energy it required. Fuck love, I thought, and I smiled at my own ingenuity. Ezra smiled back at me.

"Head down, sweetheart," I said firmly, and he ducked, docile and sweet. The shampoo beaded up and frothed into perfect opals that slid down behind his ears. Maybe they should come up with a new shampoo for kids like Ezra, something potent and authoritative named Fist or Hard-On or War. Instead his scalp was rosy and clean from Breck for Normal or Dry Hair.

After Ezra's bath we went into the kitchen and I washed the breakfast dishes while he drew pictures in an old notebook. Only yesterday Gene had left, off to Bonnie's for good (for bad, I thought), and here I was today busy with domestic gestures. Scouring powder drifted down into the sink like blue snow. I went into the bedroom and dialed Bonnie's number. They must have been waiting all night for permission or a benediction, because she picked up the

175

phone quickly and she breathed out at my ear. "Hello. Hello."

"Listen," Gene had said last night. "It's no good being like this." He meant crazy, and he wouldn't dare look at my crazy eyes and my bubbling mouth. "Come to your senses," he ordered. "Call me when you come to your senses."

"Hello," Bonnie insisted, and I hung up. I was entitled to erratic behavior. Nobody could begrudge me that.

WHEN EZRA WAS DRESSED we went downstairs and walked to the corner. We took the crosstown bus to Dr. Freedman's office on the East Side. Because this was Ezra's domain he took over, greeting the pretty blonde receptionist, then gathering a lapful of worn and familiar Golden books. I sat in my overcoat, feeling transient and sad. I picked up a copy of *Today's Health* and read a long article on contact dermatitis. God, the world was full of pitfalls. Ezra usually went in without me for his shots and his fifteen-minute talk with Dr. Freedman, who was psychologically oriented. What did they talk about in there? How did they communicate? Where was the middle ground between Captain Kangaroo and the white thighs of Dr. Freedman's receptionist? I never asked Ezra. I knew instinctively that you don't ask a boy what he says to his allergist. In turn Dr. Freedman never accused me of making Ezra wheeze. Today I would have liked a crack at him myself. I would have asked him point-blank, "Which is better for an allergic child, a dust-free broken home and a stepmother young enough to be called Bonnie or a household held together with spit?" Ezra went in, innocent on the arm of the blonde, and I sat and waited, listening to the discordant chorus of the heavy breathers around me.

WHEN EZRA WAS FINISHED we took another bus, uptown this time and into a neighborhood that was no longer expensive. It was considered a dangerous neighborhood too, where my mother and grandmother lived, and I whistled and sang to warn off muggers and rapists and the white slavers of my childhood fantasies.

"Who? Who is it?" my mother wanted to know. She

came into the kitchen, her blonde hair in wet, pinned scrolls against her head. Her fingers were splayed, held in front of her so that the polish would dry safely, yet it seemed as if she were bestowing a blessing. My grandmother had let us in, the smoke of her cigarette churning through her nostrils. She narrowed her eyes further to observe my mother. "The color is good, Frances. Nice and even." It was Saturday and they had touched up each other's hair. They sat down together at the kitchen table, crowned in identical gold. "MMH-mmh!" They both made smacking sounds with their lips at Ezra. They would hug him when their nails were dry.

"Sugar doll," my mother crooned.

"Lover man," said my grandmother. They waved their hands in the air and blew on their nails.

"Am I drying dark?" my mother asked.

"No, Frances, no. It's a good shade. You look wonderful. Some lucky guy should take a look at you."

"Oh, Ma," she said happily. Because my mother didn't need a man at all. All of her love was played out years ago and she just didn't have the vigor for the real thing anymore. When the butcher teased her and called her Honeybunch, when a half-wit teen-ager in the building gifted her with frozen Milky Ways, she was satisfied. The fictional sex lives of famous people were as real and gratifying as a warm man under the sheets with her. Real, unreal, it was all the same. She said that my father was blond, yet his picture showed him to be dark. My God, I thought, this would make three generations of us.

My father was long gone, having left us in another neighborhood I could hardly remember. And I could hardly remember him. It was difficult to separate memory from what I had been told. He was blond, my mother said. Yet the old snapshot in the bureau showed him to have darkish hair. He was tall, she insisted, yet in the picture they seem to be standing eye to eye. They met nine months before I was born. It was at a roller-skating rink and the voice on the loudspeaker called for mixed couples in a waltz number. And from that harmless nucleus of a boy and a girl dancing on wheels to the "Blue Danube," their chests swelling with the rise of the organ music, came all those unexpected growths. My grandmother, me, an apartment with all its trappings and all its snares. He ran and never came back.

I thought I would tell them about Gene. I might even have a temper tantrum here in their pink and white kitchen. After all, if blame is to be cast, you can't go back too far. Had they groomed me to be a discarded woman?

A shower of soft gray ashes fell into my grandmother's lap. She gave Ezra a dish of orange Jello, scraping the rubbery edges off with a knife. What if they gave me advice? They might say, Don't be a dope, Sandy. Don't let him get away with it. It's all hot pants anyway. Or they might say, Let him go good riddance to bad rubbish come and live with us and on Saturday we will gild your hair and shave your legs.

Ezra sucked at his Jello.

My mother speculated about how Dean Martin's and Frank Sinatra's children really feel about their fathers. I wondered where my father was at that very moment. I wondered if he ever went roller-skating again. I wondered if Gene and Bonnie were undressed together right then and how she observed his body and if she could appreciate it without ever witnessing its changes. Bonnie is small and round. She is young and sweet like a baby-sitter or a nurse or a waitress in a cocktail lounge.

"I don't care," my mother said. "I wish *I* was Nancy Sinatra."

"Ah, you're a crazy mixed-up kid," my grandmother told her. She smashed out her cigarette in an El Morocco ashtray.

They cuddled Ezra. Allergic children need a great deal of cuddling. My mother gave him a quarter. My grandmother gave him thirty-two cents. The pennies kept rolling out of his hands as they kissed him. They sent their love to Gene and they blew kisses from the doorway. Then they went inside to comb each other out. All the way down the stairs I kept silent, daring whoever waited, but my strength must have been felt and we passed through unharmed.

WE STOPPED at a luncheonette on the way home and we shared a sandwich and a soda. I bought a wooden backscratcher with a hand carved at the end of it, for Ezra. He raked it against my arm and I forced a toothy smile at him. I went into the phone booth and dialed Bonnie's number. This time Gene answered and I felt a mild vertigo at the sound of his voice. I breathed, my breath like Ezra's when he is near a shedding dog. "Huh, huh," my breath said.

"Oh, I know it's you," he said, kind and righteous as Perry Mason. "Listen, it's not the end of the world. We have to take care of certain things. We have to talk about them. Are you home now? Will you *answer* me? For Christ's sake, it's the same thing you always do. You *use* that silence on me, Sandy. It's a weapon, Sandy."

"Huh, huh." I couldn't stop that damn breathing. I looked back through the glass at Ezra who sat at the counter stroking himself with the backscratcher. His eyes were closed and his lips were open. He was giving himself pleasure. In my ear the operator whispered that my time was up and, obedient, I replaced the receiver.

WHEN WE CAME to our apartment the phone was ringing. A silent conspiracy existed between Ezra and me. He didn't run to answer the phone, I didn't tell him not to. We sat down together in the living room. Ezra stroked his backscratcher against the yellow velvet of his chair. It left long track marks in the fabric. "Do you know what Dr. Freedman said?" he asked.

I sat up, alerted, out of my slouch. "Hmmm?" I said, nondirective.

"He said he loves me."

Loves him! What a phony creep! I felt disappointed, sick at heart.

"*Everybody* loves you," I told him. The weight of this news made Ezra sigh deeply.

IN A LITTLE WHILE he went to sleep and I went back into the living room. I tried to read a book, but tears came to my eyes, magnifying the words, making them run off the page. I went into the bedroom and took off all my clothes. Generous to myself, I lit only a soft pink bedside bulb. I stood in front of the mirror. My body is nice, everything holding up well and the skin soft-textured and white. It is such a familiar body, the mole under the left breast exactly where I remembered it. I looked at myself with loyalty and affection. And yet I had to be fair. Here and there were signs that couldn't be ignored. Undefined blue shadows behind the knees. The flesh in the midriff came together too easily between my fingers. I looked at it sadly as I might at a favored dress that had not given full service.

I lay down on the bed, thinking I could probably seduce him if he were there in that same bed, in that same room, seeing those familiar blurred images through his eyelashes as he turned to me. How could he do without me? How could this happen?

I jumped up and went into Ezra's room. He was asleep, his arms out, his breath soft and perfect. I took the backscratcher from the floor near his shoes and went back to my bed. I pulled the long wooden handle along one leg and then the other. Slowly, I scratched at my arms, up and down in that same gentle rhythm. And I willed Gene to the bedside, pulling him there. He came, but I had conjured him up with his hands in his pockets and his shoulders hunched in that restless pose. He wouldn't look at me. He refused to sit in the well of bedclothes beside me. He stood at the window and looked out. "I wish the damn weather would change. It's always the same." He picked up a magazine. "Could you wear your hair this way? Do you think you would like another climate?"

Here, I said. Over here.

But he wishes that he had finished graduate school. He wishes that he could stop smoking, that he had been different with his mother and father. His shoulders still hunched, he paces the floor, and it grieves me to watch him. So I roll over, starting on my back, keeping time with his footsteps. I satisfy one place, arouse another, and I know nothing will do any good. Nothing will stop him in the whole world.

I sat up and pulled the backscratcher across my chest and I saw the pink line of the scratch fade and then rise in the pallor of a welt. It was as if I had pierced through to the heart itself.

I put on my bathrobe and went to the telephone.

Bonnie answered and her voice was tired. "Let me speak to him," I said, and Gene said, "Hello. Would you just listen for once? Don't you know I don't want to hurt you or the kid— God, it's awful." And he began to cry.

I said, "It's all right. I've come to my senses."

For Elektra

Marilyn Hacker

MY FATHER dies again in dreams, a twin.
She stands above his dying like a small
vulture in curlers, twisting her veined hands,
knowing he died before. Looselimbed in underwear
he slips from indolence to agony
on a rumpled double bed. His round
face flattens with pain. I, overgrown,
watch and fall distant till the dark green wall
is tentative beneath my palm. I fill the window light.
He is my father and my father's twin
dying again. She did not kill or save him
with her dry hands. She does not touch him now.
The screech of her nails on my cheek. I presume
too much in giving you my mother monster
rehashed in pincurls from a guilty dream
where she slaps my hand for taking cakes and cocks
on my plate and failing, failing.
I will speak to you. You are not my brother
unmasked on the river path as I long for exile.
Those black figures on the snow, too simply
dark fingers on a white thigh, establish
the clean hierarchic myth.
　　　　　　Brothers and brothers
pass under, pass over, but I never had
a brother. Lustful shorthaired virgin
bitch, borrows the voice and says,
"Your Mother is my mother. Dare."
How she bores me with her metaphors.
I would rather make love and poems than kill
my mother. "So would I. Have you done
flaunting your cunt and your pen in her face

when she's not looking? High above your bed
like a lamppost with eyes, stern as a pay toilet
she stands, waiting to be told off
and tolled out." Waiting to be told off,
Miss Bitch puts me to work for nothing
at being my own brother, with such sisters.

As Fast as You Can

Irving Feldman

Loosed from the shaping hand, who lay
at the window, his face to the open sky,
the fever of birth now cooling, cooling?
I! said the gingerbread man leaping
upright laughing; the first faint dawn
of breath roared in his lungs and toes; down
he jumped running.

Sweet was the dream
of speed that sped the ground under, sweet
the ease of this breathing, which ran
in his body as he now ran in the wind,
leaf in the world's breathing; sweeter still
the risk that he ran: of boundaries first
and then the unbounded, a murderous
roadway that ended abruptly in trees,
a cat at creamspill looking up, mysterious
schoolboys grabbing.

(Certainly, they saw him,
a plump figure hurrying, garbed in three
white buttons, edible boots, his head a hat
in two dimensions.)

Powerfully then
his rhythmic running overtook the dream
of his flight: he was only his breathing.
He said, entering his body, *Like this
I can go on forever.*

Loping and leaping
the fox kept pace, hinted, feinting, over
and under wherever, licking his chops
and grinning to the hilt of his healthy gums.
Breathing to his toes the man ran faster,
free in a world that was suddenly growing
a bushy tail and a way of its own.
No less his joy for the darkening race!

a Brilliant thought had dawned to his lips;
he understood it: thrilling absolute
of original breath! and said, *The world
desires me! Somebody wants to eat me up!*
That stride transported flying him off
earth and mystic into the fox's maw
blazing. One with the world's danger
that now is nothingness and now a tooth,
he transcended the matter of bread.
His speed between the clickers was infinite.

Tell them this, that life is sweet!
eagerly he told the happy fox
whose pink tongue assenting glibly
assuaged the pure delirious crumbs.
(Others fable otherwise, of course:
having outsped our sight, he dazzles
the spinning heavens, that fox our senses'
starved pretension. How else explain
the world's ubiquitous odor
of sweetness burning and the absence of ash?)

Shimmering and redolent, his spirit
tempts our subtlest appetite. There he runs!
freely on the wind. We sniff a sharp
intelligence, lunge and snap our teeth
at the breathable body of air
and murmur while it is flying by,
Life is unhappy, life is sweet!

The Messenger

Larry Rubin

MY LATEST FANTASY: Billy Budd
in irons, dangling above the pit in dreams
a final hour before the earth curves
into light, and I entrusted with
his reprieve. An error in the captain's
final charge (or some such technicality)
and I have the necessary papers for
his long swim upward into life—
he wakes (while everybody sleeps) and looks
with wonder at my key; no words, but I
work swiftly in the lock, and he is freed
to be what time and place and silence make
a silken sailor in the dark: a heart
as tall as dockside cranes—gorged with light
and grateful, grateful, grateful.
                              I wake in dark;
the seas are stilled.
                    I have no keys.

186

Nixon

Nicholas von Hoffman

By the time he came back here to Washington, the winner of a race between three unelectable losers, the town had made its customary accommodations. It had practiced putting the word "President" in front of his name so that, when coronation day came, it could say "President Nixon" with confident fluency. Washington must always live with whatever it's sent, so the ex-Humphrey people and the people who used to say, "Nixon! Oh, God! Never!" and the people who'd shrug a little and tell you, "Well, at least he's *our* bastard," all of them were pointing out to each other that he isn't so ugly in person, it's just on TV, and don't worry, he's smart enough to know he has to end the war. The operational definition of "smart" is getting elected.

The subterranean people adjusted differently. There's a large Washington underground made up of Federal employees—class of '60 and later—who are slowly being driven mad, every working day, at their offices. They'd go home to their modern, eight-story apartment barracks with the swimming pools and the message desks, get stoned, turn on the television set and argue over whether to adjust the color button to make his face onion purple or puke green. Then they'd sit on the floor and listen to him and laugh. That's how they got acclimated to the change.

On coronation day he rode in the back of a black limousine like all the other Presidents, but a carriage would have better suited the general feeling that this was a monarchical restoration, a contented, counter-revolutionary end to an awful and chaotic seizure of power by strangers. The ones around him fit the roles for such a drama. Agnew could play the part of the king's aging younger brother, the really bad, vengeful one kept in check by a monarch made cautious through the years of vicissitude in exile, years that teach a pretender to value the lost throne—awful, out-of-power years through which the king without a country had to suffer Goldwaterite, blanchiste plots. Kissinger could be cast as a Talleyrand or the court astrologer, an unwholesome influence, and Mitchell might be made into some sort of duke looking to get the nobility's lands returned to them.

There was that about Nixon, the tiptoeing impression of a king precariously restored. He appeared to be forgoing the major pleasures of his office for fear he'd unite the opposition to drive him into exile again. He was immoderately moderate, keeping the spasms of competitive savagery out of his mouth and letting it off harmlessly by directing the energy down his arms to make his fingers twitch. He acted like a man back from the shrink, and the city tittered it was so. Lots of people claimed they knew the analyst who'd taught him to recognize the appropriate moment to smile and showed him how to trip the switch that pulls up the mouth muscles, but Washington has thought every President of this century was crazy except Coolidge and Eisenhower. Nixon is the first they ever said was cured.

Such ideas went along with the "New Nixon" notion. There was a dispute over what the New Nixon might be. Some said he'd been theraped back to mental health, but others said, no, he'd been trapped in his own TV image and was conforming to it. The TV hypothesis was very strong. It seemed the only way to explain how he'd won the election, how he could come back eight years later and win. It had to be a new, electronically synthesized Nixon.

But it was the same Nixon and he won by slipping a little slower than his opposition. In 1960 the man had gotten 49.6 percent of the vote. Eight years later he won with 43.4 percent; in politics that can be progress.

So too, the coronation wasn't the Restoration; it was the Continuation, and that's why he didn't need to have a program or stand for anything when he ran for the Presidency and got himself elected. Nixon had no plan for the war and no plan for anything else. It probably never occurred to him that he'd need a plan because he'd spent eight years learning how to be President. For forty years in America they've known only one way to run the country and that's the way Franklin Roosevelt worked it out and

Harry Truman elaborated it. With this understanding, you don't need ideas; you need to know how to fit the job description. Both times Nixon ran he made a point of telling people they ought to throw him a vote because he was qualified by experience. He campaigned as though he'd passed a civil service exam for the position.

ON DIFFERENT DAYS Nixon looks at the job differently: Monday may be leadership day; Tuesday, national unity symbol day; Saturday is freebee day for enjoying the perks that go with the position like one-day vacations in Florida or the chance to sit next to Bowie Kuhn for nine innings. On more than one day the Presidency is a civil service supergrade in the State Department. Foreign affairs engross Nixon. That's how it should be with a President, for it has been so ever since FDR's third term.

To our last four Presidents America as a society has been a big pain in the ass. They saw the country as a three-thousand-mile-long aircraft carrier, an incubator for soldiers. The fun was in foreign policy, and you needed a country to have one.

Until 1967 the country was very good about this. It was a rich country so it could spend the money on the arms, and youth being our most overproduced commodity, there were always plenty of soldiers. That's why Nixon could say, "People invariably rally around a President in a period of international crisis." He thought he could count on that, and if it didn't exactly work for Johnson, that wasn't because of what he was doing but how he did it. Nixon could tell himself that wouldn't happen to him; he'd studied for the job.

And so we come to Cambodia. It was inevitable because in the instruction leaflet that Harry Truman left in the center desk drawer, it says that the first thing you must do is show you're not a weakling. To get your administration off to a good start, get tough with the Reds at once, draw the line, make sure they know they're not going to be dealing with Neville Chamberlain.

That formula is more important than all the psyching of the Kitsch King's masculinity problems to understand why he decided to go tenting in the Parrot's Beak and the

Lizard's Ass. He has no masculinity problems. It's out of the question. A man who calls Billy Graham into a Miami hotel room to help him pick Spiro T. Agnew as his running mate is pre-Freudian. His problems are characterological, very nineteenth century; and the talk that when he goes limp, we go to war is a literary imposition.

Cambodia had to be because one of the things that Presidents do is waste Communists. In his best-known and most instructive book, *Six Crises*, Nixon wrote, ". . . where the battle against Communism is concerned, victories are never final so long as the Communists are still able to fight. There is never a time when it is safe to relax or let down. When you have won one battle is the time you should step up your effort to win another—until final victory is achieved." In reality anything like a final victory is unthinkable. It would leave Nixon in the position of the preacher who'd learned that Satan had been popped off and the temptation to sin destroyed forever. Not only is he deprived of the pleasures of battle—and Nixon dearly believes that strife and striving make the man—but it leaves him morally idle.

This battle of free enterprise yang against collectivist yin has stayed with him, but over the years the quality, though not the fervor, of his anti-Communism has changed. When Nixon first got elected to Congress in 1946 he suffered from the Western or vulgar form of the affliction, which focuses on the enemy within. He fixed on Alger Hiss, who probably was part of a foreign espionage ring. That got him in trouble with the Easterners, the Washington lawyers and the New York bankers who concentrate on the enemy without. They tend to look on the un-American activities stuff as raucous bad taste. But those episodes in the life of our leader happened many years ago. By the time he ascended to the Presidency he'd been incorporated into the Eastern circle and was so socially acceptable that Alice Roosevelt Longworth, the arbiter of Republican style in Washington, had him to dinner.

During the 1968 campaign the antiwar faction concentrated on Humphrey. Nixon and the people around him acted as if the disruptions were a Democratic campaign phenomenon that would vanish like Humphrey and Wallace once Nixon got in there and brought the country together again. So comes Moratorium Day and Nixon is watching a football game. That's what they said he was doing and he probably was. The sports business isn't a vote-getting affectation. In the old days he'd go out with 2,800 other people to watch the Washington Senators, and you don't do that to get elected. The world's a safer place when he's at the ball park, and the people who keep needling him to get back to work are increasing the chances of thermonuclear war.

ON MORATORIUM DAY he should have stuck his head out the window and had himself a look. It was a helluva sight for any President, not merely because there were ten Astrodomes full of people surrounding the White House, and that they'd come on their own, not organized and paid for by a political party, but because of the flags. There were a quarter- or half-million Bolshis out there with all those red flags. Even five years ago such a sight was inconceivable, but they were there, just as surely as the dope fiends in the suburban white high schools. He didn't see it, or perhaps he did and it was explained away for him by Ron Ziegler, his press secretary who used to be a tour guide at Disneyland. The President of the United States had been barricaded in his own White House by tens of thousands of revolting cannon fodder, and it ought to have been a portent of the Cambodian reaction.

It wasn't. The Continuation can't understand that while it may be going on as always, nothing else is. The people always rally around the President in a crisis, don't they? They had under every President that Nixon could remember; they had no right to be disobedient with him. It wasn't fair. It wasn't possible. So Cambodia was invaded because it would shorten the war. That was the reason given and there was no way of telling whether it was thrown out in contempt or if it was a true expression of the nutty pragmatism of people who think up ultraefficient means to accomplish impossible tasks. How long would the war have lasted if he didn't invade Cambodia to shorten it.

When he metastasized the war into Cambodia, the news people who were sentenced to waste their hours in the

White House press room processing the lies could only talk in terms of psychiatry. The insanity had got to him too, they'd say. The obsession returned from the Johnson days that they were prisoners in the crazy giant's castle.

Nixon and the people around him were happy having one of their tests of internal fortitude. It's part of his strength of character credo. Nixon sees himself as a global Johnny Unitas. Six points behind, the clock is running out, the pressure is on, time for five more plays. The need is for the cold head and the superlative effort. This is a crisis. A crisis shows a man what's manly in him. A base hit in the clutch, it's the best part of life. Here is the Old Pro, coming through for another big win, in *Six Crises:*

> I stepped up my activity until I was spending as much as eighteen to twenty hours a day at my office. I deliberately refused to take time off for relaxation or "a break," because my experience had been that in preparing to meet a crisis, the more I worked the sharper and quicker my mental reaction became. I began to notice, however, the inevitable symptoms of tension. I was "mean" to live with at home and with my friends. I was quick-tempered with the members of my staff. I lost interest in eating and skipped meals without even being aware of it. Getting to sleep became more and more difficult. I suppose some might say that I was "nervous," but I knew these were simply evidences of preparing for battle. There is, of course, a fine line to be observed. One must always be keyed up for battle but he must not be jittery. He is jittery only when he worries about the natural symptoms of stress. He is keyed up when he recognizes these symptoms for what they are—the physical evidences that the mind, emotions, and body are ready for action.

There are a lot of passages like that in his writings. There are a lot in Cicero's, too. Both are military-lawyer types who live for conflict situations, where they not only shine but surpass themselves. They demonstrate their fateful strength of character and superexceed themselves into a state of stoned exaltation. They go out of their heads, the more so if they don't eat and don't sleep. You do that long enough and you'll have visions, as twenty-five centuries of mystics can verify.

Nixon was probably having a high time for himself emulating great men in those first couple of days of Cambodia, while the people in the press room were going around holding on to the walls. But then he had a real crisis, not one induced by moral hyperventilations, or even by the threat of the Chinese inserting themselves into that ruined peninsula. There were insurrections at home. They may not have been as harrowingly frightful as what it looked like after Martin Luther King was murdered, but the White House was worried. The disturbances might spread beyond the campuses; they could jump to the ghettos or even to the armed forces.

On the official level, the Nixon people lost their tone of undeviating certainty; the coherence of the lying fell off in rattled panic: yes, they weren't bombing North Vietnam, no, that wasn't a bombing raid, it was supportive, reactive, interdictive, suppressive, contingency harassment, bombardment fire; we're only going in twelve miles, twenty miles, thirty miles and that's definite, but you shouldn't rely on those figures as more than advisory, and about yesterday's denial of the supportive, reactive, suppressive contingency bombing, yes, we lost some airplanes, no, not shot down, we lost track of them and while they were gone they dropped a few bombs, where? In North Vietnam but only reactively.

A SCENE IN THE WHITE HOUSE PRESS ROOM

THE CREW-CUT PRESS AIDE who stands at parade rest while Ziegler does his monologues begins inviting people backstage. I am approached and led into Ziegler's office. Outside the window is Nixon, hands behind his back, talking to Kissinger, strolling on the lawn, maybe still grooving on his crisis euphoria or maybe he's already crashed. The four at Kent State have already been killed; two more will die at Jackson shortly.

John Ehrlichmann comes into the room. He's part of the Presidential staff that's always being reorganized. Each time it happens the columnists with the inside information write that Ehrlichmann has come out on top, cutting off so-and-so and so-and-so from access to the President. That holds for a few months, then there is another reorganization and one learns that Ehrlichmann has again come out on top.

"I'm sure John would like to hear your ideas," Ziegler says.

"Suppose you're right about Vietnam," I begin, and they make as if I'm about to give them the unique word, instead of being one among who knows how many reporters they've run through their office. Most of us believe against certain knowledge that if only we could get in there and tell them, they'd listen. So I am here in the White House and the President's man has said he wants to hear. You don't have to be a politician to be infatuated with your own possibilities.

"Suppose you're right about Cambodia," I continue, "suppose you're right about the military situation, suppose you're right about everything, don't you see you still can't fight this fucking war?" I fancy that the word hasn't been spoken in the building since Lyndon Johnson. I also imagine that bad language may make them pay attention. "In a democracy, see, fifty-one percent is good enough to build a road or exempt the oil companies from taxation, but not to fight a war. You gotta have ninety percent for that, and your boy didn't pull that in the election. That cocksucker was elected to end the war, not spread it."

Ziegler is a two-expression man, blank and smiling. No frowns, no pensive looks, no screwing up in distaste, it's the blank or the smile. The blank is for when you're speaking; the smile is for when you're finished and he's about to talk. Having a conversation with him is like playing tic-tac-toe with a computer.

"People'll feel differently when it works out. Opinion'll change when it's a success," Ziegler says. An efficient organization silences all opposition by declaring high quarterly dividends.

"Millions of people don't give a shit if it's a success. Christ almighty, they don't even know where Cambodia is much less want to conquer it."

The President has gone from the lawn.

"We know that. We're pulling out. We're withdrawing. Vietnamization is working."

"Oy!"

"As people see that the President's policy is a success, they'll support him."

"If you keep pushing this way, these kids are going to burn down the country. Get off people's necks."

Ehrlichmann says something to indicate that things are nastier than he'd like to see them. There is more talk about the stock market, the businessmen, the different kind of people who've had it. Ehrlichmann agrees it is serious, remarking it has probably cost Governor Rhodes of Ohio the primary. I repeat the prediction of bloody trouble. Ehrlichmann replies, "We're counting on leaders like yourself to keep things calm."

Leaders like who?

We're doomed.

THE NORTH VIETNAMESE lost their laundry and their rice in Cambodia, but the administration lost its cherry. Up to then, they'd tried to depict themselves not as aloof, but as detached. Thoughtful enough to care, but not to be dangerously involved. After Cambodia that went fluey. A few days after the scene in the press room, Nixon broke out of his cup of pass-defending blockers and went bombing over to the Lincoln Memorial near dawn to wake up kids who'd come in for the demonstration. After he'd finished unzipping sleeping bags and shocking the drowsy with the realization that The President was on them in their dreams, Ziegler's office gave it out that he was praying to the shades of departed chief magistrates. A lot of people said it was a schmaltzy grandstand play tearing after the young, chatting about surfing at four o'clock in the morning. But contrived or not, it was still crazy. Rational means applied to insane ends.

The word was sent to cabinet officials—do likewise, communicate. Full secretaries, assistant secretaries, and deputy secretaries were shagging people off the streets and asking them, "What do *you* think?" as if the whole country would fall for the politicians' old con of asking for advice. While everyone was communicating and relating and dialoguing and, who knows, maybe even T-grouping in the Treasury Department, the White House seemed more afraid. More guards, more cops; at night it looked like a gangster's suburban home, spotlights playing away from it toward the street to light up any attempt to cross the fences, run over the grass, and break in.

It was during this period that Finch fell apart and had to be recalled to Father Nixon's bosom. Every administration has a secret good guy, somebody close to the throne on whom the enlightened fasten their hopes. Under Johnson it was McNamara who was generally believed to be a political schizophrenic, a war hawk by day and a dove by night. It was said he would sally out to dinner parties and bemoan the tragedy of it all, offering imprecations to the god of the District of Columbia to bring an end to it. If the gossip is to be believed, McNamara did his Walrus and Carpenter act over ten thousand brandies and after-dinner cigars.

Under Nixon Finch assumed McNamara's role. He went to parties, was polite, and kept a smiling silence when unorthodox ideas were expressed in his presence. The idea gained currency that he was a liberal, though a search of his political record shows he's seldom done more than hold Nixon's coat. In the regime of player-coach J. Paul Peptalk, Finch became the guy who follows him around carrying the clipboard. But that was to come later, after his employees and his incapacity to do good or evil chased him out of HEW, a department where the administration's vacuity of thought is undisguisable.

From medicine through education, Finch sploshed, banning dangerous drugs, reinstating them, desegregating and resegregating as Nixon and friends tried to devise a set of deals and compromises that would drop the national decibel count, but the results were more provocation of the already irascible. No one could be mollified, no progress could be made because the limit of Nixonian thinking was to tinker and make minor adjustments in the machinery of his predecessors. There was no strategy, Southern or Northern, there was only the perpetual ad hoc accommodations.

The younger HEW employees rebelled over everything

but particularly the race issue, integration. Finch was too weak to slap them down as they would have elsewhere. He agreed to meet with them and his weakness was taken for liberalism. But the meeting could never be held. The duplicity, the vacillation, the confusion, the lying, the changing of minds and intentions, the firings and resignations over what the government was doing in civil rights couldn't be defended or explained. There would be bussing, no bussing, there would and there wouldn't be forced integration, it would be voluntary-compulsory law enforcement but not jammed down anybody's throat with five hundred million dollars to aid the you-name-the-number of school districts that were unitary de jure and de facto, and there was Cambodia, too.

The night before the meeting, Finch was crying out at another dinner party, "What am I going to tell them tomorrow?"

"Tell them you quit," somebody said.

Donald Rumsfeld, the OEO administrator sitting across the table from Finch, said, "Don't. You liberals are always jumping out the window and committing suicide."

But he didn't tell Finch what to say, so the man moaned on until his wife led him away.

The next day the paralysis of will manifested itself in his arm, the use of which he lost. They took him to the hospital. When he got out the coach told him he was benched and brought him over to the White House, where he took a pay cut but got a new uniform with a quarterback's number and was allowed to sit next to the Old Pro through the rest of the game and carry the clipboard.

ON THE CLIPBOARD is the game plan. The economic game for which the coach plans is, like baseball, one of small differences: ease off on the inflation pedal, push down a point or two on employment, adjust the liquidity valve. As in so many other matters, there's been no significant change in the way the economy's been handled for years, except perhaps the deals are more public. In the old days FDR didn't go over to John L. Lewis' office, Lewis came to see the President. But Nixon pops over to visit Meany and sits in on meetings of the AFL-CIO executive committee. They may bicker some over small items but there's general agreement on the big ticket—support of the war, support of centralized labor power and centralized business power. It is many years past that Big Labor had reason to fear a Republican incumbency.

The game plan isn't economic planning but manipulation to favor certain groups. The dislocations of production, labor, and investment grow worse and more obvious. Carpenters never made more money but it's getting harder and harder to get a cobbler or nurse; the telephone service disintegrates in New York, Boston, Chicago, and Miami; our steel plants grow obsolete; the power shortages get worse; there are too many teachers but not enough classrooms. In the networks of handclasping cartels, trusts, friendly agreements, and supportive government action it's increasingly difficult to get the labor, the capital, and the technology where it's needed. The free market economy, which did these things imperfectly and with intolerable swoops of the business cycle, is replaced with a form of managed chaos in which all established and powerful tendencies, irrational and deleterious as they may be, are reinforced, and all weak ones, as useful as they might become, are squashed.

If the stock market has swindled and speculated its customers into near bankruptcy, Nixon proposes to have the government insure it; if the Penn Central Railroad is run recklessly and inefficiently into the red, give it money. But the proposal which went the farthest toward destroying the distinction between private and public is welfare reform. Under it, not only all the people without income, but working people with inadequate incomes would receive supplemental assistance from the government. In the ordinary Nixonian fashion, the idea was introduced as a work-incentive plan, a scheme that would eliminate all the cheating and abuses that both politicians and despairing citizens have complained about for so long. In reality it outrages both conservative and liberal-radical principles. On the one hand it destroys the distinction between being on or off the dole, which conservatives have believed is a necessary incentive to get lazy people to work. But on the other hand, it not only subsidizes cheap labor business operations but will eventually make the government the co-employer in the nation's sweatshops. In time, as the government guaranteed-income figure rises, every dishwasher, laundry worker, migrant worker will discover the government making up the difference between a living wage and what his boss is paying him. Union organization will be discouraged, some of the unloveliest people in American private enterprise will be having their labor costs subsidized, and the way will be open to blacklist political and social rebels from employment on a scale and with an efficiency heretofore impossible because of the fractured, uncentralized nature of so many business operations. Under this scheme, a student kicked out of a college for raising political hell may find himself not only banned from government employment and companies with large defense contracts but from most of the obscure occupations that our political misfits use to survive.

Nixon's new Emergency Housing Act offers another example of the Continuation's traditional response to the need to improve real wages or redistribute wealth. It permits a subsidy on mortgage interest rates for all middle- and lower-income families, which is nice for the insurance companies and the savings and loan associations while lessening the pressure on employers to pay a livable wage.

NONE OF IT WORKS; none of it will work. And Nixon is a man fighting not to give you the satisfaction of knowing the itching powder you poured under his shirt is driving him crazy. He's not going to let you know you got his goat. He's determined not to scratch in public, but he terminates every press conference in such a way that you can imagine him breaking into a run the moment he's out of sight and leaping upstairs in the White House, discarding his clothes as he runs so he can throw himself in the shower where the dye in his hair will run smoky rivulets as the water gives him relief.

Then he goes to his office to concoct new policies which will be in accord with what's written in the How To Be President booklet. He's stuck in the New Deal because he's a Wall Street lawyer, a totally absorbed member of the Eastern Establishment, a phrase which doesn't mean some salaried Ivy League professors and a klotch of Episcopal clergymen, but the big money people centered in New York and six or seven other cities. *They* haven't found Nixon more difficult to guide and direct than the four Presidents who came before him. Check the continuing influence of a David Bruce or a Douglas Dillon.

Domestically, our President, bathed in Dial for all-day protection and doused and sprayed with the most effective itch suppressants, has looked over the country and misread what he sees. He's back in Truman's day when it was how many jobs, not what kind or what they pay. The misallocation of billions of dollars by the government and by the centralized financial power allied with it eludes him, except that he's learned it's fashionable to speak of reordering priorities and changing over from a war- to a peacetime economy. He doesn't understand the line on the political violence graph inclining ever dangerously upward. Beatings, shootings, bombings, snipings, street brawls, and other new acts of political terror frighten and madden more people, but as he sees it, it's time to freeze the ball, to call running plays into the line and eat up the clock. That is the way to win another election, and if the country is lost, it will happen after he departs. The very bad years, if they come, will be after his second term ends. What he's doing is giving away the time needed to avert them.

But some kind of new play was needed, so he called the New Federalism double-reverse end-run razzle-dazzle. In 1964 Goldwater had made a big thing of returning power to lower and more accessible levels of government. How that might be done remained unarticulated. It was for Nixon to make a show of doing something. Characteristically, what he did was make a show of efficiency, while keeping the power in Washington. The regional districts of the federal bureaucracy were made to coincide geographically and to headquarter in the same cities; much noise was made about rebating federal tax money, but not taxing power; noisiest of all was the bringing-government-to-the-people publicity stunt which has him surfacing almost anywhere to hold meetings of small consequence with five or six state governors. Any actual transference of power can't be taken seriously, not only because it contradicts the New Dealish impulses of the Continuation but would louse up every major lobbying and corporate interest agglomeration which uses Washington to divide markets, administer prices, and protect themselves from trust-busters, ecology idiots, consumerists, and Nader Raiders. State governments, especially state legislatures, are cheaply bought, but they don't stay bought; they're easier for the citizenry to get at and are liable to take out after the automotive industry or some other patron of the team.

The coach isn't having any of that kind of New Federalism, or new anything else, but he isn't obdurately insensitive to everything. He knows the war and the war weapon budget is too high, that the strategy of forcing the Soviets to bankrupt themselves on armaments is backswinging on us; his transportation secretary knows he's got to stop pouring ready-mix; his housing man knows that sheltering more and more of the population in mobile homes won't do, his air man knows we're getting sick from breathing, and his water man knows we're getting sick from drinking, and if he had a race man, he'd know we're already sick from hating, but none of 'em knows it well enough or strong enough to put away the game plan, and if they did, they'd be benched. The Old Pro is calling off-tackle plays, watching the clock, hanging in there, playing for a tie.

The Writer's Situation: III

The following responses conclude the symposium that has been running in the past two issues. Its purpose is to inquire into the changes that have occurred in writing during the last decade, as writers themselves have experienced them. In order to focus the discussion, we asked contributors these six questions, which they were free to answer as they chose:

1. Why do you continue to write? What purpose does your work serve? Do you feel yourself part of a rear-guard action in the service of a declining tradition? Has your sense of vocation altered significantly in recent years?

2. Do you believe that art and politics should be kept apart? Has this belief changed or grown more complicated during the past decade? What influence has the politicalization of life during this period had on your work?

3. What are the main creative opportunities and problems that attract and beset you in your work? Which movements, tendencies, writers, if any, do you find yourself identifying with or supporting? Which ones do you oppose?

4. Has writing entered a "post-modern" era, in which the relevance of the great modern writers (Joyce, Eliot, Mann, Faulkner, et al) has declined? If so, what seem to be the literary principles of the post-modern age? If not, what principles of modernism are still dominant and valuable?

5. Has there been a general collapse of literary standards in recent years? Are you conscious of a conflict between your past standards and your present ones?

6. Has literary criticism and journalism kept pace with, and faith with, the best fiction, poetry, and drama produced in the sixties?

Benjamin DeMott

I GO ON WRITING because I'm interested in describing (understanding) new patterns of thought and feeling that worry/mystify/excite me. Since I'm a country-dwelling, piece-writing, middle-aged English teacher/family man, not a full-time novelist living at the hot center, most of the descriptions or "understandings" I come up with are bitty, lack a uniform tone, and are occasional in origin. An attack of melancholia at a wedding anniversary dinner party sets me to writing about husbands' attitudes toward wives, for instance. Supper-table fights with sons and daughters young and old—23, 19, 13, 6—about received parental values produce other stuff. A month on a faculty-student steering committee during and after the Cambodia strike starts me on a long college-life/rad politics journal. Someone asks me to review a book or stand a culture-watch at an interesting site, and I do that. And there are self-sponsored library-loafing hunts for guidance in Emerson, Peirce, Dewey, and earlier and later American great souls that end up often in some writing . . .

Digging further into the purpose of working, I see that the urgency does derive from the nature of the new states of mind or patterns of feeling I just mentioned. What can be said about these in a paragraph? Let me name a few assumptions that seem to count. People believe that:

1. The character of human experience and human time can be altered: life is infinitely more pliant than our fathers knew.

2. The character of human experience and human time should be altered: present forms of experience (teaching, learning, loving, governing, worshipping, entertaining, child-raising) are jails, barriers to flexibility, dehydrators of the human moment of being.

3. The wanted alterations will not take place merely through adjustment or liberalization of political or social opinion. Society must teach itself wholly new values, accept major new additions to its old declarations of blessedness, viz:

Blessed are those who interrupt, for practically everything now ongoing can profit from derailment or bad bumps.

Blessed is the sense of Possibility, for it is the prime energy-source of men who interrupt.

Blessed is Openness (open personalities, open classrooms, openness to experience in the large), for it alone protects interrupters from falling into habit and passivity of their own.

As goes without saying (right?), many human and social problems flow from such assumptions. (The great god Possibility encourages people to be fantasts, forgetful of the responsibilities that begin in probabilities rather than in dreams, forgetful too of the human needs for markers, maps, sightlines, balancing points, cherished solidities of terrain, as well as for fresh pastures new.) As also goes without saying, the new assumptions, and the emergent sensibility they're shaping, create big opportunities. (First among them is the chance of ending social and moral compartmentalization, moving toward fuller development of the human capacity to constructively imagine, and care about, lives different from one's own.) The aim of describing all this—I admit it sounds dull and teacherly—the aim in "understanding" it, is to teach yourself how to be adequate both to the problems and the opportunities.

But talk of aims presupposes a writer with a feeling for the big picture. I don't qualify, true. The recurring questions for me are homely: how much New Thought can actually go down in a stable middle life? How can a human being (as opposed to History in the large) cope, in his own local limited head, with the tilts of assumption and belief now occurring regularly in living rooms, classrooms, committee rooms?—Your children are polite but detached about jobs and marriage, yours included; your young employee promotes herself to full partnership; your neighbor's wife goes fiercely women's lib; the first-rate novelist in your hand says, Quit, civilization is finished; your friend and former student, fifteen years out, berates you in print for not being a Maoist in 1955; your college's top science graduate, cropped, scrubbed, polite, informs you commune life is absolutely the only thing; you wake up on the morning of a new decade resolved to explain to yourself as clearly as you can what exactly happened during the ten-year night before and you can't say a word . . . What then follows? What sequences of feeling and thought shape a man's innerness in such circumstances? What kinds of order can a mind work out for itself? This is the writer's work as it shows itself to me.

Reading over the last sentences I see that the part about a mind working out order on its own implies solitariness, independence, originality, etc. Trash that, as children say. I couldn't claim to find myself "identifying with or supporting . . . any movements, tendencies, writers" and so on—but I do know that scouting around for a personal perspective, something more than "correct" descriptive labels, means leaning hard on other minds. Scores of them, including many that aren't household words. A practiced leaner, I try to name the leaned-ons as I go (this past week I leaned on men named John McDermott, Albert Hirschman, and Richard Sennett—one philosopher, two social scientists). Literary journalism may have declined but the quality of social observation has, I think, improved. In any case it's the example of the community of "other minds," unselfish clarifiers, flexy heads, men of hope, relishers who've stayed at it, hunting down our meanings—it's that example that gives me the sharpest sense of what a genuine possibility-culture would feel like, and puts the matter of "literary collapse" in saner perspective. Study that community and you glimpse the "open future" here in the present, even as you pick up, if not the secret of preserving an elegant standard, truth about how and why to go on going on.

Stanley Kauffmann

1. GREAT WRITERS often answer these first questions frivolously. Hamsun said he wrote to pass the time. Céline (like others) said he wrote for money. Lesser beings can't afford to joke. I have had different reasons for writing at different times and have written different sorts of things, but for the last dozen years or so, I've been increasingly

aware that I write to certify my life. As far as I can. Or, put another way, I write because I know I'm going to die. Writing strengthens the consolations of that fact, as well as lessening its starkness, by persuading me that I have lived. I'm not so silly as to mean immortality—of any kind. I mean simply that some use of my life helps to assure me that it is really happening and makes the eventual conclusion not only less ridiculous but almost (as long as it is indefinitely postponed!) welcome.

For the last dozen or so years, I've been concentrating on criticism, of several kinds, and as Frank Kermode said in an earlier contribution to this symposium, criticism is a "service industry." One hopes to contribute to that "industry" in as rich a way as possible, and this provides a sense of purpose which is sometimes more definable than that available to the primary artist. (Hayden Carruth's essay on Lowell is more "useful" than Lowell.) There is also another, autotelic purpose. Oscar Wilde said that criticism is the best form of autobiography; possibly true, but possibly too retrospective. Criticism is also one of the best forms of para-existence. It provides a concurrent Kauffmann who seems to me a bit more interesting than the one I am enclosed in.

2. POLITICS IN ART is, to me, simply one of the options, available to those who want to use it. I have no prejudices for or against those who do or do not use it. But I have always been keenly interested in politics, and I am more and more convinced of the inutility of political art. (Assuming that it *is* art, not mere transmogrified propaganda.) The audience for good art is always severely small as against the whole population; thus good political art will be read or seen only by a small part of the body politic and, since views within that group differ, will probably affect only a small part of that already small group. How many people have had their minds *changed* by *Guernica* or *The Caucasian Chalk Circle* or *One Day in the Life of Ivan Denisovich* or *The Triumph of the Will?* I think it is clear now that politics is simply one more subject for art, like springtime or love for lyric poets.

In a way I have been most strongly influenced in the

past decade by the *lack* of politicization: by the growing sense of irrationality and incompetence and conspiracy in government and by the growing sense of impotence that all this produces in us. Governments are not stupider or wickeder than they used to be, but modern consciousness is wider and is more aware of shortcomings. Yet in another way I enjoy (the precise verb) the reaction of many people, particularly young ones, brought about by this wider consciousness. With them and like them, I often march and sign protests, and like them, I see a growing polarization in the world. But, unlike them, I am not very sanguine about the outcome. For two reasons.

First, I think the "enemy" is much stronger and more resourceful than they like to contemplate. Second, even if the "enemy" should be crimped or overcome, I think that my friends would soon become the new "enemy." I cannot imagine a realized Good Society. I think that, in the long run, one simply exchanges pluses and minuses. When men stop trying to right wrongs and relieve oppressions, the world will once again become prehistoric mud; that seems inarguable. But Algerians now persecute Algerians; and Castro has his political prisoners.

Politics begins in the psyche, not in manifestos or in governmental or economic structures. The most cheering aspect of the best young revolutionaries is that they see that the real revolution must be in values. Historically, revolutionaries have been puritanical; the best of the new revolutionaries are spiritual. This certainly does not enhance their chances for success, but at least it guarantees a longer struggle.

As I am the person who holds these views, these views affect my work: in several ways. Relevant artwork is juxtaposed inevitably with these views—and has, in fact, affected these views from time to time. Unrelated art—the film or play or novel that has nothing to do with these subjects—is all the more precious when good. Not, most certainly, as escape but as contribution. The more I see and read, the more interested I am in complexity and contradictions, in the artist who can reckon with complexity and contradiction or even genuinely corroborate them.

3, 4, 5. I DON'T "OPPOSE" any good artists. This is not a circular argument that ends by defining good artists as the ones I like. I recognize—to name a wild assortment—that Carl Dreyer and Michel de Ghelderode and John Hawkes and Elizabeth Bishop are good artists, although little of their work affects me. I don't oppose them. And I think it is highly risky to oppose "movements," as such. One is repelled by the intellectual and aesthetic sloth of such theater ensembles as the Performance Group and the Living Theater and takes a firm stand against the anti-traditional theater, but then one encounters Jerzy Grotowski and a breath of life.

On the other hand, the clamor for a New Sensibility makes me uneasy. If one follows the path of the New Sensibility, it leads to an infinitely fragmented series of solipsist systems, without any common currency of standards, even highly flexible ones. Art then becomes something like sex appeal; the subject in question either has it or hasn't. But this isn't even the point of the New Sensibility. In one of the most noted pronouncements on the subject, "One Culture and the New Sensibility," Susan Sontag celebrates the new artists "engaged in programming sensations," then says that the New Sensibility "does not mean the renunciation of all standards: there is plenty of stupid popular music, as well as inferior and pretentious 'avant-garde' paintings, films, and music. The point is that there *are* new standards, new standards of beauty and style and taste." Unfortunately, Miss Sontag doesn't tell us what these new standards are.

"Post-modern" is a clumsy term (will it be followed by post-post-modern, like off-off-Broadway?) but it is unavoidable, I suppose, since the term "modern" has a generally accepted meaning and since that meaning no longer embraces much of the new. But possibly our whole trouble here is semantic. Maybe much of current dissension and discomfort comes from our insistence on continuing the use of the term "art," about which we expect "criticism." Maybe we need a brand-new term to describe, say, a pile of bricks on an art-gallery floor, which differs from any other pile of bricks only in that it was put there for non-brick purposes. If it were called by some new name instead of "art," things might be better for everyone, including the brick-piler.

This is not an ironic threnody about the "end" of art. I do not mourn the "end" of the novel or of the theater, and would not lift a finger to help "save" either of them or any other art. Art is a function of society; as long as an art form is functioning, there seems little point in demanding less than the best from it. If society wants it, then it ought to function at the highest level possible. But if an art form withers as a form, then probably its function is no longer needed and it is being cancelled or supplanted. While novel-writing lives, criticism and aesthetic education also live by discerning qualities in novels. But to fight the "death" of the novel is to be an aesthetic Luddite.

Jeremiads are easy, and cultural history does not include many clean sweeps. "Everything has been said, and we have come too late, now that men have been living and thinking for seven thousand years and more." This particular knell for new books was sounded by La Bruyère in 1688. Still, few would contend that fiction holds the center of the contemporary sensibility. People seem to be turning elsewhere for imaginative sustenance and stimulus—to film and rock and social activism, which last is taking on some of the traditional functions of art. (And some fiction is making itself look foolish by trying to keep up with this shift, by trying to be something it is not.) Recently I happened to ask a group of five or six university film students what they thought of *Light in August.* Not one of them had read it. This is not a "collapse of literary standards" but of literary appetite. I was shocked, but I wonder how pertinent my shock was. These students were intelligent, alert, concerned. Will the world of mind and spirit be worse off in their hands than in those of the "Faulkner generation"? I don't think a categorical answer is possible.

As to my own standards, there has certainly been change, but I am less conscious of "conflict" than of what I believe is enlargement. The new gets added, and if it contradicts the old, that doesn't mean conflict, it simply means that I and the world have lasted a bit longer and have acquired some more contradictions. When I first read *Waiting for Godot,* I thought it was fascinating but eccentric. Now it seems to me concentric; the cosmos almost seems to be situated within that play. But I don't like Chekhov less; he now seems to lead to Beckett. Nor do I like Shaw less. Beckett doesn't wipe out Shaw, the last great optimistic writer; Shaw (among other things) helps to explain why even the nihilist Beckett bothers to write plays.

Or, as Borges says in his essay on Hawthorne:

"Wakefield" prefigures Franz Kafka, but Kafka modifies and refines the reading of "Wakefield." The debt is mutual; a great writer creates his precursors. He creates and somehow justifies them. What, for example, would Marlowe be without Shakespeare?

6. The distinction between criticism and journalism is unfortunately apt—particularly in literature, because there are at least a couple of dozen really good literary critics in this country who don't often review new works. A gifted novelist can go through his whole life without getting a newly published book reviewed by one of those good critics. This is a pity. If good critics wrote regularly about new novels, the literary situation might not be night-and-day different, but it would be different. Instead, those good critics make only occasional forays into the journals and thus have no steady and steadily refining influence. Much of the time, the reviewing of new books, even books by gifted people, is left to dray horses or typewriter tap-dancers.

The situation in drama is both less and more pitiful. Less: because there are not nearly as many good drama critics as literary critics (and most of the few good ones are not now writing regularly), so there is not all that much good critical talent unapplied. More: because the steady application of even those few critical talents might have helped to hasten some deaths, speed some razings, revise some values, and nourish valuable theatrical life. What we mostly have instead are ebullient gabblers and nonebullient gabblers, and some others, particularly young ones, who think that, if they include the phrase "decadent bourgeois culture" in every review, they show profundity.

But, in terms of the economic use of critical resources—the expenditure of intellect and time on material that is worth it—I daresay that, by and large, the American theater has had the criticism it deserves. American fiction has not.

Alvin Greenberg

ECONOMY

THE REAL CHALLENGE is, quite simply, how to say as much as possible in any given moment, or poem, or paragraph. To say little is to lie, because in any human situation, and perhaps in the situations of the purely physical universe as well, the truth of things is dearly related to how much is happening at once. The sheer quantity of life is what impresses. The question for me is, simply, how to extract the quality of that, without falling absolutely speechless—as, awed by it all, I am apt to do in conversation. One of the ways of the moment is to turn to multimedia techniques: to seek a multiplicity of stimuli which attempt to reproduce or parallel the stimuli of experience. But imitation is not necessarily good art, which is to say, not necessarily the most effective extraction of the quality of the quantity of experience. There are other ways and possibly, even still, purely verbal ways, less imitation than distillation perhaps, or less even that than the creation of a world, someone in it, and his experience of, with, its subtle complexity, through what I would call, and try to make, a synchronous prose, in whose simplicity much happens. Take two simple sentences, obliquely related to one another (they concern the same person) and place them side by side—or, as we do with sentences, one after the other. Things happen, complex things not inherent in either of the sentences but closely related to the complexity of the universe from which those two sentences spring. And then someone knocks at the door to call me to the phone, but you tell them to take a message, I can't answer, just now.

WALDEN

WHAT YOU DO is to venture out into the world, and it doesn't make any difference whether that world is called "writing" or something else because what you take out there, primarily, is yourself, plus whatever baggage you've accumulated along the way. And simply because what you are taking out there is basically your self, the baggage is likely to prove incidental and of little use: toothbrushes and techniques, passports and polished prose, can trip you up as easily as take you on; and though they may at times satisfy certain necessities or be of some convenience, they add little to your presence there, to what you may be doing. You go out because it's a world out there and you want to find out what it's like and how you can do there, and finally, maybe, what you can bring back to tell others about it—which is to say you go out in a spirit of adventure—and the point is that you can't make that journey with technique, but only with your self. If you make it with technique you will bring back technical things: beautiful photographs, exotic fabrics, unforgettable characters—things of much value, no doubt, which may be as much as most people want of your travelogue. But if you make it with your self, then when you return you can bring back something for others to explore as well: the human experience of that world—and that is invaluable.

SOLITUDE

SINCE I FIND that the main creative opportunities for my writing are synchronous with the main creative opportunities for my life, I write, and continue to write, for the same reason that I live, and continue to live: because they are (there are) *creative* opportunities. And the creative opportunity that I try to make both center and circumference of all this is the exploration of that world, that human universe, in which life and art, Hebe and Horspfal, you and I, the children, the children's friends, and their friends' friends too, not separately, exist. The density of that world is incredible, and if we constantly glide through it, each of us, in a curious solitary fashion, practiced and yet as if for the first time, we are, still, not inaccessible to what we can be given of the experience—not the knowledge, I think, but the experience—of someone who has, in some way, been there before. We follow the track his words leave; if it is a linear path, why, then, perhaps we should remember that that is the way we all move still, one foot and then the other. Each step a step into the possibility that the writer has shown us is there.

VISITORS

WE ARE, after some years of dubious apprenticeship, what we make ourselves to be, in the simple acts of our day-to-day re-creation. What we create, *is*. Where we live, we are: in an open territory of our own making. We can change; therefore we are responsible for what we are. The same thing that is true for myself is also true for what I write: *it is*. That is the most important thing that can be said about it, though such a statement is also apt to have some relevant corollaries. For example: It is, therefore it can be encountered. (Disquisition: Consider what it means to bump into a work of art. Is it, in any way, different from a human encounter? Does not the story also grope about in the dark for contacts?) For example: It is, therefore it is self-sufficient. (Disquisition: As much as anyone, but who doesn't need a sympathetic ear, patient understanding, the possibility for a developing relationship? Kiss me.) For example: It is, therefore . . . anything can happen. (Disquisition: Its very existence is an affirmation or why take the trouble to write. Hence there is no such thing as pessimistic art.) For example: It is, and then . . . Q.E.D.

THE PONDS

WHAT KIND OF WORLD is it that I see to write in/of? I would describe it, with an assist from Samuel Beckett, as the world of the reversed metamorphosis: "The Laurel into Daphne. The old thing where it always was, back again" (*Watt*). Things, people, back in the world and a world of people, things. Not a world characterized by (Jungean, Yeatsean, Taoist, Christian, or generally religious) "symbols of transformation," in which men, like Christ, are raised from mortal existence to eternal essence, but rather just the opposite: a world where even ideas, once believed to be insubstantial, become real and tangible. And are they not? Touch a man's ideas and watch him wince.

HIGHER LAWS

I AM A great believer in the comma (more than the semicolon because more graceful) as a means of helping things go on and on, which is the way they do, and in the parenthesis also because of the way it has of letting one slip inside the present and add yet another dimension, without which no suggestion of the complexity of that simple moment might be possible, and even, in moments of desperation, in those paired sets of dashes which allow one, in between, to dash off in some other direction, or on some parallel course, whose exploration cannot be postponed a moment longer, and especially in the notion that the most beautiful phrase in the English language is "and then," which elucidates and so makes real those lives that we call our fictions, which is the true connective by which all things are held together and so made possible, which is what keeps us afloat in this sea of events out of which the stories of our lives drift, which is like the punctuation mark of extension, those three little dots that know no bounds and open up, for the writer, the infinite possibilities of the future. That, after all, is what one writes for. As when I am given this chance to express myself on my writing, and then . . .

BRUTE NEIGHBORS

SINCE I TAKE the human experience to be the most significant part of any literature, any art, I am left basically unconcerned with whether this means following an old tradition or developing a new one out of the "post-modern" era. Perhaps there is some truth in the argument that in the old ways only the old things can be said, experienced, but this means neither that the old things weren't, still aren't, worth encountering nor, conversely, that saying things in new ways can guarantee saying new things. Things are what they are: personal things, political things, rocks that tumble in my dreams, vegetables I bark my shins against in the dark, you, always, for sure. Meanwhile, a subscription to the latest technique soon expires, and manifestos are never mistaken for works of art. They too are what they are, bump bump. So by the "human experience" in literature I mean, specifically, not a defection to technique, either rear or avant-garde, but an overriding concern for what it is like to go bumping along in this world we all share, more or less, and in which technique is relevant not to the time or to movements but only to the author's individual version of this experience, and its expressive needs, as he conceives of them. These collisions too are a part of that world and unavoidable.

HOUSE-WARMING

PUT THE POETS back in their poems.

FORMER INHABITANTS; AND WINTER VISITORS

IT DOES NOT MAKE any difference where the beginning is. Borges begins with ideas, but it is the things in his stories, the experience with things, as they go by, *and then* take on reality in their passing, that is important. Beckett turns ideas inside out throughout the process of his fiction so that what counts is less the ideas themselves than the fleshy lining to which we see they have been stitched all along. Nabokov is constantly casting lines out to "significant ideas" but it is the people, the things, the experiences, to which the other ends of those lines are attached, which complicate and compromise the ideas, that are most important. Conrad, perhaps, ends with ideas, but by that time they have been so muddied by the reality from which they have been derived that they are no longer separable from that mud, that reality. Fiction is not refined, or refining. If I begin with a paragraph full of ideas, I soon find myself, if the story is going to go anywhere, among things, real things, and then the beginning must be lopped off because the presence of events has rendered it superfluous, irrelevant, wrong. Talk about "ideas taking shape" becomes, in literature, talk of shapes—the shape of an object, a conversation, a gesture, your cheek—not talk of ideas.

THE POND IN WINTER

THROUGH OTHER WRITERS one can step out on the thin ice of creativity and measure its possibilities. Reading them allows one to see where, in relation to one's self (a tautology, of course: what other true relation is there?), people and things are, the world, and its creative potential, is. Other writers become the Archimedean points that allow one to weigh the atom of his own existence—

> . . . in a sense, all poetry is positional: to try to express one's position in regard to the universe embraced by consciousness is an immemorial urge. The arms of consciousness reach out and grope, and the longer they are the better. Tentacles, not wings, are Apollo's natural members. . . . While the scientist sees everything that happens in one point of space, the poet feels everything that happens in one point of time. Lost in thought, he taps his knee with his wandlike pencil, and at the same instant a car (New York license plate) passes along the road, a child bangs the screen door of a neighboring porch, an old man yawns in a misty Turkestan orchard, a granule of cinder-gray sand is rolled by the wind on Venus, a Docteur Jacques Hirsch in Grenoble puts on his reading glasses, and trillions of such other trifles occur—all forming an instantaneous and transparent organism of events, of which the poet (sitting in a lawn chair, at Ithaca, N.Y.) is the nucleus.
>
> VLADIMIR NABOKOV, *Speak, Memory*

—of which each of us remains his own nucleus.

SPRING

here a woman turns into a tree
and back again

a tree a woman a tree a woman . . .
christ won't you hold still for a minute!

"take cold baths and long walks. alone"

the forest is full of trees i know

CONCLUSION

POETRY. *vt* (1) to bump into (2) to grab hold of, like this: one tries to meet the sometimes subtle, sometimes crude shades of variance that make up the individual's encounter with the world, the step forward (aside, backward, down) into those areas surrounding the self, whatever they are filled with, *or* the rambles of the self, a live and moving presence, among other presences, and hence the pressure of presence as the pressure toward encounter. What have you bumped into lately? Not "plot" or "character," not "structure" or "meaning," but whatever is there, and happening, in its unpredictability, most of all in its solidity, and then maybe even more so in the need—for the sake of survival—to meet it in the tangible and independent reality of its own being, its own taking-place. Consider what the parable of the blind men and the elephant would have been like if, in the end, there had been no elephant.

Hilton Kramer

1. WHY DO I WRITE? I write criticism, reviews, "studies" of artists and writers, and I write now for essentially the same reason I felt moved to begin writing over twenty years ago when I was still a student. I found then, and I still find today, that no book, no poem, no work of art, no form of artistic expression or body of ideas, is fully "real" to me until I have attempted to come to terms with it in written form. Writing about a work of art puts me more deeply in touch not only with the work itself but with my own response to it and with those values, emotions, ideas, and sundry revelations that form the essential link between the work and my own life. This, for me, is the function of critical writing: to make us more *conscious*—conscious of what we think and feel and know or will never know—than we should otherwise be. One hopes, of course, to contribute to the consciousness of others—one's readers—but the task begins with oneself.

My own sense of the critical vocation has not significantly altered in recent years. What has changed is my sense of the conditions in which criticism is now practiced. There has been, I believe, a significant decline in the value that is placed on critical intelligence. There is a greater yearning for a direct, unmediated response to aesthetic experience—for admitting art directly into the bloodstream, so to speak, without the intervention of conscious intelligence. This yearning, which is fundamentally a desire not for aesthetic experience but for self-surrender, is destructive of a great deal more than critical discourse. It is destructive of art itself in its highest forms, for in its highest forms art exists in a symbiotic relation to critical intelligence. To sever that relation is, inevitably, to deny art one of its principal resources. The denial has attained, in some quarters, the status of a biological imperative. To the extent that one feels the pressure of this denial as a real force in our culture, a critic like myself cannot help but feel that he is serving a declining tradition.

2. THE QUESTION SUGGESTS that one still has a choice, and thus betrays its liberal origin. It assumes that our culture is going to remain spacious enough, politically, to accommodate such choices. As a liberal myself, I would like to believe this is true. But the pressure to convert art into a medium of political action grows more insidious every day, and the margin of choice narrows. The very notion of artistic and intellectual disinterestedness is under suspicion where it is not already under a sentence of death, and more and more people seem to regard such a notion as "objectively" reactionary.

In the relation of art to politics, I believe criticism has one indispensable function to perform: to keep both art and politics acutely conscious of each other's aims, substance, and prerogatives. Ten years ago it was necessary to underscore the fact that, as Trotsky once observed, "from the point of view of an objective historical process, art is always a social servant and historically utilitarian." But now the danger is not that we shall overlook the social implications of art, but that we are tempted to reduce art to nothing *but* its social implications. We have drifted into the politicization of art without ever having produced a significant body of social criticism of the arts, and this is one reason why we are ill-prepared for the current crisis. The pendulum swings from an extreme aesthetic formalism to an extreme politicization, while the large middle ground, where art and politics really meet and touch our lives in very different ways, is simply ignored.

3. IT IS PRECISELY on this middle ground, where the problems of art reveal themselves to be scenarios for coping with the pressures of life (including social and political life) as they impinge on the individual sensibility, that I find the "opportunities and problems that attract and beset" me in my work. I am opposed to all reductionist theories, whether of the formalist or political variety, which seek to impose an historical "line" on what forms, styles, materials, subject matter, or point of view an artist may be permitted to use. I am interested in these theories as a cultural phenomenon, however, for they constitute in themselves a significant scenario for coping with the unprecedented complexity of current artistic problems. I am not conscious of "identifying" with any movement or tendencies.

4 and 5. THESE QUESTIONS must be taken together, for it is precisely to the extent that the "relevance" of the great modern writers has been felt to be in decline that literary standards have collapsed. Where our literature has sustained its most conspicuous vitality—in our poetry—it is inseparable from the principles of the great modernists. It is in prose fiction that our literature has really collapsed. Fewer and fewer novelists feel capable of conceiving a large fictional structure in which the lives of others—the society of their own time—are given imaginative priority over the vicissitudes of private fantasy. The large ambitions of the masters—Proust, Joyce, Mann, James, Faulkner, Flaubert, Kafka—have not been sustained. Among the most talented younger writers of fiction, it is Beckett and Borges who have become the models. Both are marvelous writers of very small compass, and each seems already to have exhausted the vein he invented. The sheer energy that once made the novel such a large factor in our consciousness of the world we were living in is now dissipated in

other enterprises—mostly journalism and autobiographies. The latter have an undeniable appeal. They speak directly to our sense of history and our sense of the self. But even at their best they offer us only the materials of a great fiction—not the thing itself. To the extent that these non-fictional forms have been made to serve the functions of fiction, I suppose we have indeed entered upon a "post-modern" period.

6. LET'S DISTINGUISH between literary criticism and journalism. The latter flourishes, the former fades into oblivion. Literary journalism has vastly inflated the importance of almost every work of fiction and drama that has come to its notice while literary criticism has hardly noticed the existence of such work. I am not sure this is a mistake in the case of the drama, for drama itself can hardly be said to exist. Its principal interest for some years has been in the number of intelligent critics who agree to pretend that this moribund enterprise has somehow retained its claim on our attention.

The major critical dereliction of the last decade has been in the field of poetry. On this, the richest of our literary achievements, the one boasting the largest number of interesting talents, the greatest variety of statement, and the keenest insight into the relation of the interior life to the quotidian world—on this, criticism and journalism have been almost indistinguishable in their silence. This is, among other things, a reminder of the way serious criticism, insofar as it still exists, has followed the practice of journalism in choosing its subjects from the literary marketplace. Which is, I suppose, another way of saying that criticism is no longer serious. There is Richard Howard, of course, whose book *Alone with America* is the shining exception that proves the rule. It is the poets who have kept faith with the standards and ambitions of the modern masters. When we have understood why this is so, and why there has been so little recognition of their accomplishment and so little attempt even to comprehend it, we shall understand a great deal more about the real decline in our literary culture.

Richard Hugo

1. I DON'T KNOW why I write and I doubt that my writing serves a purpose. I don't feel that I'm guarding the tradition and I doubt that the tradition is declining. The real reasons why a poem is good are probably not subject to radical changes.

Yes, my sense of vocation has altered in the last five years. Before I started teaching at the age of 40, I never took what I was doing for a living seriously. Most jobs are absurd. In fact, to hold a job much of your energy is spent convincing yourself that what you are doing is important. If you can convince yourself, you can usually fool the boss and hold your job.

Frost, I think, said that a poet could either farm or cheat on his employer. I believe that's true, at least to the extent that a poet never gives to a job what he gives to a poem. If he did he'd be suspect. I'm too lazy and incompetent to farm, and for many years I've been cheating on my employer. When I teach literature or composition, as I often have to, I'm still cheating. But when I teach poetry-writing I'm not. I consider the teaching of poetry-writing my vocation and I work hard at it. I guess I never had a vocation before unless writing poems is a vocation.

2. WHEN I TRY to write a poem on politics, or anything in the "public arena," I end up with nothing. Either I already know how I feel about the subject, or else I sense moral and social pressure to simulate feelings I don't necessarily have. Whatever the case, my imagination becomes impotent. There's no chance to discover feelings I was previously unaware of, to say something I never expected but always wanted to say, to surprise myself on the page.

There may be other reasons why writing a poem on a public matter—politics, pollution, racial injustice—is hard. One is that they ought to have poems written about them. Another is that in the mind they suffer the natural death of anything subject to prolonged mass attention. (Try to write a good poem about Niagara Falls.) If I tried a "public poem," I'd probably use *ottava rima* and try to be funny.

But most of our problems aren't funny and I'd feel uneasy.

I don't think art and politics should be willfully kept apart or willfully allied. I keep them apart because I'm limited as an artist. If I could write fiction I'd try to take on public matters. Fiction writers don't suffer from the illusion that anyone believes them, and this gives them a broader range than is available to a poet. If you know your audience doesn't believe you (who really believes a novel?), you have a chance to change its mind. I believe fiction writers can cause things to happen, visions of the world to change, values to alter. Probably that shouldn't be their prime concern when writing. Melville wrote *Moby Dick* without thinking about changing anybody's vision of the world, I'm certain. But he changed mine all the same.

Finally, in writing about public subjects you may end up arguing with others instead of yourself, and as Yeats pointed out, the result is rhetoric and not poetry.

3. I NEED LITTLE in the way of opportunities. Paper, pencils, a brief look at something most people ignore, and a considerable amount of self-delusion. None is hard to come by. The only reason I don't write more is that I write out of obsession and tend to repeat myself. I do this in conversation too and am often boring. I fight the urge to write the same poem over and over. This is the only limitation on my opportunities, and it is self-imposed and obviously necessary.

My most serious problem is the risk that my poems will cause my personality to deteriorate, though this has happened only once. The risk is difficult to explain because I don't understand it well, but it appears to be something similar to the aesthetic notion of the "mask becoming the man." When I'm writing I often become the speaker in the poem. For me, this is necessary for the words to be meant or to sound meant (actually the same thing in a poem), but it is not normal or healthy. As long as this "being the speaker" stops when I'm not writing there's no problem, but for a long time once it didn't stop. I started to act out the poem in social situations. This is oversimplified I'm sure and probably not an adequate explanation but it's the best I can do.

It started I think around 1966, but during the next two years it became more involved and serious. I was isolated in southern Italy in late '67 and early '68. By "isolated" I mean that I had no one to speak English with for better than three months. The only relations I had *in my language* were with the poems I was writing. With no chance to express myself socially in English, even in daily trivial give-and-take, which I found is more important than I'd ever imagined, I became disoriented and fell back on the poems, on the speaker in my poems, for social intercourse. My behavior became bizarre, especially in Spain where, for the first time in months, I was back with English-speaking people. This state continued in England. Since I like people and have a real need for people, it was frightening to find my personality so oddly compulsive that I was inviting social rejection. It was so unnerving in fact that I wanted to stop writing for good. With my language, more or less my language, going on about me in England I began to re-establish my normal social self. But I didn't recover completely until I was back in Montana at my job and with my friends. I like lots of friends in real life and none when I'm in a poem. The two worst fears I had during this time: I would never get a woman again because I had grown so odd; I wouldn't be able to get along with people and would lose my job.

For the rest, I identify with and support any poet who plays it alone and pays no attention to fads, movements, or trends, and I resist poets whose ambition to be a part of "literature" affects the way they write.

4. PERHAPS IT ISN'T the relevance of modern poets that has declined but their influence. In poetry, for a long time and even as recently as fifteen years ago, Pound and Eliot seemed to have considerable literary power (I think much of it was imagined) and this power in part came from the way they wrote poems. But too many interesting poets were writing poems in a variety of styles and methods, and once we looked around we found that the tradition, far from being one of inherited linear influences, was one of diffuseness. The contemporary poet can write a poem any way he wants to. This is a psychological disadvantage and

can lead to attempts to will originality and stage meaningless literary revolutions. The most recent phony development I've run into is the man who decides anything he does is a poem. In this way he can be called a poet even though he can't write.

I remember that Roethke tried for years to have Faber & Faber (i.e., Eliot) publish his poems. Poets took Eliot's position that seriously. It's hard to believe now. None of my contemporaries that I know would recognize one poet as being so powerful that they would solicit his approval and acceptance. The whole idea seems silly.

Pound's criticism remains influential. Some of his ideas about writing seem as vital and fresh today as when he wrote them. But the idea that a poet can, as a result of his method of poetic composition, seize and hold literary power, is obsolete. I'm glad it is. Now maybe we won't have to suffer through those attacks on Eliot that seemed to appear every three or four years.

5. No, I don't think literary standards have collapsed. At any time much garbage is hailed and rewarded and so standards always seem to be collapsing at the moment. No, no conflict between my past and present standards—I'm still trying to write a good poem.

6. CRITICISM OF POETRY is better now than it was twenty years ago. The "New Critics" were more careful at times, and more thorough, but they were less human than the present reviewers and critics. They tended to talk about poems as if the poems were refrigerators rather than something written by men. The tendency of the more recent critics and reviewers of poetry, like Richard Howard, Louis Simpson, James Dickey, the late Randall Jarrell, and Donald Hall, is less toward analysis and more toward illumination and appreciation, and I think it's healthy. Often, the New Critics analyzed poems not in an effort to help us to the poem but to establish and defend a theory about "what poetry really is."

Neil Compton

1. WHY DO I *continue* to write? The italicized verb is a bit ominous, possibly implying that it would be more sensible to do something else. (Make underground films? Stage living theater? Take up the guitar?) If I were a young genius with (in Samuel Johnson's definition) "a mind of large general powers accidentally directed in some particular direction," I might very well try to avoid being accidentally directed toward a literary career. Not all things are possible in every age, and ours does not strike me as a good time in which to emulate the achievement of a Chaucer, a Shakespeare, a Milton, a Dickens—or even a T. S. Eliot.

However, I am not young, not a genius, and not a poet, dramatist, or novelist. There continues to be a demand for my kind of workaday prose. I write critical and discursive essays for reasons that are as valid today as they presumably were when the Greeks invented expository prose two and a half millennia ago. They include the innocent satisfaction that comes from helping to interpret, clarify, and transmit the complex traditions of a culture controlled by the written word; and the less innocent sense of power that this function gives to the scholars, priests, and popularizers who perform it.

Much more valuable to me personally is the intellectual discipline involved in even a fairly trivial act of composition. Johnson (that heroic writer whose spirit seems appropriately to be haunting these paragraphs) once remarked of an eloquent gallows testament that there is something about the prospect of being hanged that wonderfully concentrates the mind. For me, the moral equivalent of hanging is an editor's deadline: it can induce insights and visions of order of which I have not previously been aware, or force the recognition that ideas which once seemed clear and articulate are really confused and contradictory. (The trouble I've had with my not-so-startling replies to this damned questionnaire is an example.)

Since writing is so useful and gratifying an activity, I

don't think that there is anything rear-guard about it. The development of new media has ended the near monopoly of books as repositories of wisdom and information, but writing and print will always be indispensable. Zealots like McLuhan may blame the world's ills on the visual, linear bias of typographical man, and we may agree that centuries of reliance upon print have fostered habits of mind which need to be corrected. Nevertheless, the even more serious deficiencies of the new media are steadily becoming apparent. *The CBS Evening News* is no substitute even for the front page of *The New York Times*, let alone for such institutions as *Barron's* or *I. F. Stone's Bi-Weekly;* and the Public Broadcasting Laboratory hardly threatens to drive *New American Review* out of business.

In consequence, my sense of vocation as an unashamed middleman has not changed, in spite of the sneer of a contributor to the first collection of responses to this symposium in *NAR* 9 (p. 72). Fate and personal inclination have radically shifted the focus of my mediating activities, however. Ten years ago, I was an orthodox academic with special interests in Shakespeare and eighteenth-century English literature. Today, I try both to keep up my professional standing in these fields and to resist the intellectual curse of specialization; but I devote more and more time and energy to the most modish of new scholarly fields—the study of popular culture and the media that transmit it. Though both editors and readers are often more responsive to even casual efforts in this field than they are to solider pieces of work on the classics, a certain aura of intellectual unsoundness surrounds the subject—wrongly, I believe. *Laugh-In, Highway 61 Revisited,* and *I, the Jury* may be infinitely inferior to (say) *As You Like It,* Dowland's lute songs, or *Roderick Random;* but, as part of the contemporary world, they uniquely reveal certain important aspects of our common life, and the scholarly techniques of rhetorical analysis, iconography, and socio-psychological interpretations pay off handsomely. Of course, a shift toward an interest in the culture of commercial entertainment can and sometimes does involve a change of values so radical that it amounts to a virtually new vocation after all. I have tried to resist this.

2. ART AND POLITICS cannot be kept apart, but they obviously tug in opposite directions. The question of which should prevail, and to what extent, can be answered only by individual artists speaking out of their own sense of history. Sometimes conflicting loyalties allow no satisfactory resolution, and a potentially tragic choice becomes necessary.

Today, the moral and intellectual disorder of most advanced industrial societies may create an almost inescapable dilemma for writers and artists—particularly if they are citizens of one of the violence-deploying superpowers. Fifty years ago, the religion of art would have enjoined its adherents to dramatize such a situation to the full, so long as it contributed to the production of masterpieces. Now, however, technology and instant communication directly implicate each one of us in every act of violence or oppression committed by the state in our name; artistic immortality has become less urgent than relevance and immediacy. Both the past and the future now seem so insubstantial that the demands of the present assume irresistible authority. Many artists who might once have lived lives of remote creativity now feel tempted to embrace radical action or polemical journalism or both.

As the citizen of a country fortunate enough to play only a minor role in international politics, I am able to gaze south over the border with a kind of detached sympathy. As of this writing, English-speaking Canadians can still enjoy the luxury of vicarious commitment—savoring the ideological passion, the moral indignation, and the dangerous strategies of their American friends, without having to take any of the risks.

Meanwhile, many of our French-speaking compatriots are obsessed with the cause of Quebec separatism to a degree which makes the American preoccupation with Vietnam and racism seem almost mild by comparison. If these fierce emotions are ever translated into mass political action, the border traffic in detached sympathy may have to start moving from south to north. In such circumstances, where no *status quo* is beyond challenge and constant change is taken for granted, reality itself can only be conceived in political terms.

3. OVER A HUNDRED YEARS AGO, Matthew Arnold identified the main intellectual endeavor of his time as an attempt "to see the object as in itself it really is." Today, most of us seem to have given up this perennially unsuccessful quest. Many who are not otherwise disciples of McLuhan act as though they believed the medium were the message. Others turn Sainte-Beuve upside down and assume that *l'homme, c'est le style!*

The task is immensely complicated now that we experience "reality" through the mediation of so many different agents. Nevertheless, I believe that the function of criticism at the present time continues to be what Arnold described so long ago. Because this involves an awareness of the practical obstacles to experiencing objects as in themselves they really are, the contemporary critic (particularly anyone concerned with the media) is unprecedentedly dependent upon help from nonliterary experts. Riesman, Giedion, Lifton, and Chomsky (to name a random few) have been at least as useful to me as (say) Frye, Kermode, Fiedler, and Howe. Just as the camera has taken over some of the representational functions once performed by painters, so these broadly speculative theorists are performing tasks which were once the province of novelists or playwrights, such as George Eliot and Ibsen.

The answers to subsequent questions will probably suggest which contemporary movements, tendencies, and writers I generally support and oppose. The saintly model whom I personally would emulate if I had a fraction of his genius and integrity is Erich Auerbach. This fugitive from Nazi savagery wrote *Mimesis*—his great loving study of the representation of reality in Western literature—in Istanbul while the Second World War threatened to destroy all that still existed of the great humane tradition whose history he was illuminating. It was an act of faith which should inspire others to seek similar principles of order amidst the apparent chaos of media and messages.

4. CLASSICS ARE always relevant, by definition, and the masterpieces of modernism are surely classics. Nevertheless, few contemporary writers attempt to emulate the combination of monumentality, erudition, and intellectuality that

marks the achievement of the early twentieth-century masters. I see no sign though of any tradition so new and different that it requires to be labeled post-modern.

We are sweating out the last and most uncomfortable stage of a process that began with the revolt against "reason" of Rousseau and Blake. The consequences are depicted with fearful clarity in the works of the great moderns; they all dramatize the confrontation between a European ideal of order, harmony, and rationality that is somehow going awry, and newly released primal energies and instincts which, however deeply satisfying and dynamic, are potentially subversive and destructive. The resolution of modernist works is usually ironic, somber, or tragic, because no one since Blake has successfully reconciled order and energy in a single affirmative vision.

By the nineteen-seventies, things seem to be falling apart as predicted. On one hand is the tradition of Mann's Serenus Zeitblom (and Erich Auerbach) and the more conservative writers and critics. It is detached (but not indifferent), learned, archeological, and contemplative. A superlative example—in its limitations as well as its virtues —is Sir Kenneth Clark's brilliant series of BBC television lectures, *Civilisation*. While the cameras reverently and sometimes even erotically explore the great artifacts of Western culture, Clark's commentary places each object in its proper relation to the others and to ourselves as inheritors of the tradition. It is a masterpiece of enlightened popularization. But this virtuoso production becomes in the end a kind of *Times* obituary for the whole way of life it celebrates; the very sureness of Clark's judgments testifies poignantly to the fact that the story he has to tell can be completely known only because it has an end as well as a beginning. Sir Kenneth undoubtedly overvalues the Apollonian element in European civilization, and this tempts him to hold his obsequies a little prematurely. Nevertheless, not many contemporary writers still feel able to pledge unqualified allegiance to what is left of this tradition.

On the other hand is what Lionel Trilling used to call the counter-culture, based upon the celebration of impulse, vitality, and irreverence, and hostility toward establishments, history, and detached intellectualism. Although the counter-culture is strongly anti-academic, its proponents are increasingly well represented on university liberal arts faculties. Thousands of undergraduates now groove to the songs of those anti-traditional sirens long before they learn much about the sort of high culture Sir Kenneth Clark holds dear. As Oscar Wilde said in another context, they are led directly from barbarism into decadence.

I can't identify wholeheartedly with either of these antagonistic parties, nor am I capable of bridging the gap between them. Forced to make a choice, I should have to line up with Zeitblom and Clark, but it is still possible to live uneasily in the margin, and there, for the moment, I take my stand.

5. COLLAPSE IS a strong word, but literary standards are undoubtedly in a state of confusion. Twenty years ago, I subscribed to a set of critical principles which may have been mutually incompatible but seemed to work in practice: the linchpins were *Scrutiny* for doctrine, the New Criticism for procedure, and social democracy for values. Like my hero F. R. Leavis (though I admired him this side of idolatry), I looked in literature for colloquial richness and vigor, "a reverent openness to life," and moral seriousness (not solemnity).

I am not exactly hostile to these qualities today, but they no longer seem so essential to artistic achievement. I find myself admiring works in which they are not manifested—the writings of some black humorists, for instance. There was a time when I used to begin each new course with a sort of critical credo. Now, I'm afraid that I allow my standards, such as they are, to emerge gradually during the lectures and discussion. I should certainly have a hard time articulating them explicitly—particularly to a skeptical class of senior undergraduates.

The reasons for this rather shameful middle-class revisionism lie less in ourselves than in our stars: living as we do in an age in which a moral code centered on production is giving way to one centered on consumption, in which a once endlessly bountiful nature has suddenly revealed strict limits, and in which the whole system of transmitting and storing information has been revolutionized, we should be acting like David Riesman's tradition-directed primitives if we continued to behave and talk as though nothing were happening.

6. DURING THE late nineteenth and early twentieth centuries, urbanization and a vastly expanded reading public created an ideal climate for the flowering of literary criticism. This relatively new discipline, whose early masters had been Dryden, Addison, and Johnson, was designed to instruct readers rather than writers and stressed explication rather than magisterial judgment. Its golden age lasted about forty years, from the end of the First World War to the late nineteen-fifties. It came to an end partly because the academic marketplace encouraged reckless overproduction, with consequent deterioration in quality of work and satiety among the audience, and partly because the rise of new media such as cinema, television, and tape recordings has disturbed the ecological balance of intellectual life.

It is probably this imbalance that has caused such an astonishing renaissance of the higher journalism over the past two decades. Many "creative" writers now dabble in it on a full- or part-time basis, and some of them are destined to be remembered for their journalistic ephemera rather than for their serious work. The new media inundate us all willy-nilly in a miscellaneous sea of information and shallow experience. It threatens to drown us. What the media fail to provide, because they cannot, is the kind of explanatory and analytical detail that will add meaning to at least some of what is communicated. No one can really understand the TV news unless he also reads a newspaper. Wars, riots, demonstrations, politics, and generational conflicts are one-dimensional for all but the immediate participants, without the perspective provided by the written word. Good journalism of all kinds is, in fact, absolutely necessary to the maintenance of humane reality amidst a chaos of images. Fortunately, there is quite a lot of it around.

Last Words

Sylvia Plath

I DO NOT WANT a plain box, I want a sarcophagus
with tigery stripes, and a face on it
round as the moon, to stare up.
I want to be looking at them when they come
picking among the dumb minerals, the roots.
I see them already—the pale, star-distance faces.
Now they are nothing, they are not even babies.
I imagine them without fathers or mothers, like the first
    gods.
They will wonder if I was important.
I should sugar and preserve my days like fruit!
My mirror is clouding over—
a few more breaths, and it will reflect nothing at all.
The flowers and the faces whiten to a sheet.

I do not trust the spirit. It escapes like steam
in dreams, through mouth-hole or eye-hole. I can't stop it.
One day it won't come back. Things aren't like that.
They stay, their little particular lusters
warmed by much handling. They almost purr.
When the soles of my feet grow cold,
the blue eye of my turquoise will comfort me.
Let me have my copper cooking pots, let my rouge pots
bloom about me like night flowers, with a good smell.
They will roll me up in bandages, they will store my heart
under my feet in a neat parcel.
I shall hardly know myself. It will be dark,
and the shine of these small things sweeter than the face
    of Ishtar.

Correspondence

To the Editor:

MR. THEODORE ROSZAK's "The Artificial Environment" [*NAR* 9] strikes me not as an original essay but as one more addition to the series of attacks on industrial society by literary intellectuals. Certainly it is time to consider the gaps in this familiar argument.

1. Who is this "technocrat" or "social engineer" whose "diminished mode of consciousness" is engulfing us all? I find no explicit definition. At one point, "the heights of technocracy" are defined as "the federal government, the federal courts, the military, the major corporations, the big foundations, the universities, and the liberal intellectual establishment" (p. 133). No *new* class is named in this list, and none of its members has any intrinsic relation to the advancement of technology. "The technocracy" seems to be merely another name for "the Establishment."

2. Mr. Roszak contends that "the technocracy" gains an ever-increasing share of power because it holds a monopoly of technical skills. He envisions established centers of power growing even stronger by utilizing the services of technical workers. He does not explain how such a concentration occurs, and if he attempted, I do not know how he could succeed. Technical innovations may work *against* the interests of established power centers in that they stimulate disruptive ideas and emotions. Television encourages the majority to buy, but played a part in encouraging the people of Watts to riot. Our educational industry has produced the scientists and engineers who landed a man on the moon —and also produced Abbie Hoffman and Jerry Rubin. Obviously the effects of technology are highly variable and serve contradictory trends.

3. Mr. Roszak contends that technological society is undemocratic since only a few can understand its techniques. But from the citizen's point of view, only the *effects* of a technique are relevant; the technique itself is not. Technology provides methods for fighting in Vietnam, but does not justify the American presence there. The United States is not in Vietnam due to the manipulations of a technocratic class but because a majority of Americans believe in the war. Mr. Roszak will not face this fact. I myself do not believe in the common man's values and see no point in lip service to a sentimental populism. To say that the common man is brainwashed by advertising and televised moonshots is merely to present a thin disguise of my own point of view.

4. Mr. Roszak apparently believes that technology is invulnerable, in the sense that anything desired can be achieved. He cites examples of failure, that in fact illustrate bad effects—e.g., pollution, noise, and urban congestion resulting from widespread use of the automobile. To carry his horror story to its proper conclusion, he must depict technology as omnipotent and omniscient, simultaneously insisting that it does not know the true dimensions of human nature. His self-contradiction suggests the following argument.

An outright technological failure (that does not perform its intended function) usually results from a fundamental planning error. For example, the F-111 failed because its designers attempted to combine two quite different planes in one. If Mr. Roszak's religious vision of man is correct, then "the technocracy" should experience difficulty in manipulating its subjects, since a fundamental factor of human behavior would be ignored. His pessimism implies a lack of confidence in his own values. If human wants and needs are completely programmable, the technological society ought to function beautifully. Who would agree to this, after living through the sixties? "The technocracy" has not even succeeded in the one limited objective of controlling inflation, despite drastic remedies. Solutions to other conflicts are even further away, for there is not even any body of technical method to deal with them. Perhaps our society, considered as an integrated system, suffers from fundamental design errors, like the F-111. These "design errors" are fundamental inconsistencies in our culture. An example is the fact that our culture requires stereotyped masculine and feminine role-playing although it lost all need for this some time ago. If we would use technology in building the society we want, everyone must first dig up his own emotions, sort them out, and live by what they imply. In fact, the technological point of view implies a revolutionary and utopian approach to social problems.

5. Apparently Mr. Roszak's fundamental cause is the defense of religion against the claims of science. I thought that the domains of science and religion had been settled long ago. But when he carries intellectual antiquarianism to the point of attacking objective knowledge as "alienated" there is nothing left to say except that we are in a psychotic world where nothing is perceived except through a fog of personal emotion. No culture could think this way and survive.

If we are to abandon technology, most of the world's population must die of starvation or disease and the remainder live a short and brutal life. Where would Mr. Roszak be, in this "humanized" world? One of the clergy, no doubt.

Edward Brynes

Poughkeepsie, New York

CONTRIBUTORS

Walter Abish lives in New Jersey. A story of his appeared in *Confrontation* (Spring, 1970) and a collection of his poetry, *Duel Site,* was published by Tibor de Nagy Editions last year.

M. F. Beal (b. 1937) has published two stories in *NAR* (3, 7). She has recently completed a first novel.

Robert Chatain (b. 1944) received the 1969 George Dillon Prize from *Poetry.* One of his stories, "The Adventure of the Mantises," appeared in *NAR* 7.

John Clayton (b. 1935) teaches at the University of Massachusetts. He writes that he is "taking part in building my house and in building a radical movement."

Neil Compton (b. 1920) has been the television critic for *Commentary* during the past five years as well as a professor of English at Sir George Williams University in Montreal. Mr. Compton's essay on Marshall McLuhan appeared in *NAR* 2.

Robert Coover (b. 1932) has published his fiction frequently in these pages. His most recent book is *Pricksongs and Descants* (Dutton). In the past year or two, he has been writing films and plays.

Benjamin DeMott (b. 1924) teaches at Amherst, has published two novels (*The Body's Cage* and *A Married Man*), and three collections of literary/cultural criticism, the most recent being *Supergrow* (Dutton).

Irving Feldman (b. 1928) is the author of three collections of poems; the most recent, *Magic Papers,* was published last year by Harper & Row. He teaches at SUNY at Buffalo.

Allen Ginsberg (b. 1926) recently recorded "William Blake's Songs of Innocence and Experience Tuned by Allen Ginsberg" for MGM Records (FTS-3083). He writes that "last few winters spent outside cities learning music milking cows & goats."

Alvin Greenberg (b. 1932) edits the *Minnesota Review* and has contributed fiction, essays, and poems to a variety of little magazines. Two of his stories appeared in *NAR* (8, 10).

Marilyn Hacker (b. 1942) lives in San Francisco and edits *Quark* (speculative fiction) and *City* (poetry). Her poems have appeared in *Arx, ManRoot, The World,* and other little magazines.

Daryl Hine (b. 1936) is the editor of *Poetry.* His collection of poems is titled *Minutes* (Atheneum), and he has recently completed a metrical translation of *The Homeric Hymns.*

Richard Hugo (b. 1923) has published two volumes of poetry, *A Run of Jacks* and *Death of the Kapowsin Tavern.* He teaches at Montana State University.

Steve Katz (b. 1935) wrote *The Exaggerations of Peter Prince* (Holt) and *Creamy & Delicious* (Random House). He is presently working on a screenplay titled "Grass Land."

Stanley Kauffmann (b. 1916) is film and theater critic of the *New Republic.* A new collection of his film criticism (*Figures of Light*) will be published this year by Harper & Row. Mr. Kauffmann also teaches at the Yale Drama School.

James Kempton (b. 1944) graduated from Harvard in

1967 and is presently unemployed. He has written for *The Village Voice* and *WIN Magazine*.

Rudy Kikel (b. 1942) is a teaching fellow at Harvard. His poems have appeared in *The Lion Rampant* and *Hub*. He is writing a Ph.D. thesis on "the imagery and idea of serenity in Walter Pater."

Hilton Kramer (b. 1928) is an art critic for *The New York Times*. He also writes for the *New York Review*, the *New Republic*, and other journals.

A. J. Litwinko (b. 1944) studied at West Virginia U. and U. of Pennsylvania, and is teaching this year at Bryn Mawr. This is his first poem to be published in a periodical.

Cynthia Macdonald (b. 1933) teaches at Sarah Lawrence. Her poems have appeared in *Prism International*, *Envoi*, and *Canadian Forum*.

Norman Martien (b. 1939) writes that he has "retired from a brief career of university teaching and is working at new schools, catalogs, and a book of essays and fiction about the sixties." An early version of "Getting Out of Schools" appeared in *Reflections*, a literary magazine published at Washington University in St. Louis.

William Matthews (b. 1942) is co-editor of *Lillabulero* and teaches at Cornell. His first collection of poems, *Ruining the New Road*, was published last year by Random House.

James Merrill (b. 1926) won the National Book Award for Poetry in 1967. His most recent collection is *The Fire Screen* (Atheneum).

W. S. Merwin (b. 1927) brought out two books last year— *The Carrier of Ladders* (poetry) and *The Miner's Pale Children* (prose).

John Morgan (b. 1943) is currently writing a novel about paleontology. Several of his poems were included in *The Young American Poets* (Follett).

Harold Ober (b. 1948) is a graduate student at the University of Massachusetts. His fiction has appeared in *Vortex* and *Pornocopia,* which he also edited.

Sylvia Plath (b. 1932; d. 1963). "Last Words" will appear this year in a volume of Miss Plath's uncollected poems titled *Crossing the Water* (Harper & Row).

Stanley Plumly (b. 1939) teaches creative writing at Ohio University. His first book of poems, *In the Outer Dark,* was published last year (L.S.U. Press).

Michael Rossman (b. 1939) has appeared in the *American Scholar, Rolling Stone, Ramparts,* and other places. The child named in his essay was a boy.

Larry Rubin (b. 1930) taught American literature last year at the Free University of Berlin. His most recent collection of poems was *Lanced in Light* (Harcourt).

Paul Spike (b. 1947) graduated last year from Columbia College. A collection of his stories, *Bad News,* will be published this year (Holt).

Frank Stanford (b. 1948) is an undergraduate at the U. of Arkansas. This is his first published poem.

Frances Starr has published prose pieces in *Provincetown Review, Film Culture,* and other little magazines. Miss Starr is a free-lance writer and editor living in New York.

Nicholas von Hoffman (b. 1929) is a columnist for the Washington *Post.* His books include *The Multiversity* (1966), *We Are the People Our Parents Warned Us Against* (1968), and *Left at the Post* (1970).

Paul West (b. 1930) published last year a novel, *I'm Expecting to Live Quite Soon,* and a memoir, *Words for a Deaf Daughter,* part of which appeared in *NAR 3*. His next novel, *Caliban's Filibuster,* will be brought out by Doubleday (Paris Review Editions).

Allen Wiggins (b. 1939) is a reporter for the Cleveland *Plain Dealer.* This is his first published poem.

Hilma Wolitzer (b. 1930) has published several stories, one in *NAR 5*. She lives in Syosset, New York, with her husband and two daughters.